Abandoned
Love

Rosie Houghton

Matador
9 Priory Business Park
Kibworth Beauchamp
Leicestershire LE8 0RX, UK
Tel: (+44) 116 279 2299
Fax: (+44) 116 279 2277
Email: books@troubador.co.uk
Web: www.troubador.co.uk/matador

This is a work of fact. Nevertheless, some names of people and places have been changed to protect
the privacy of the individuals concerned. Grateful acknowledgement is made for permission to reprint
excerpts from the following copyright works:

The Lord's Prayer as it appears in Common Worship: Services and
Prayers for the Church of England (Church House Publishing 2000) is
copyright @ The English Liturgical Consultation and is reproduced by
permission of the publisher.

ISBN 978-1780880-617

British Library Cataloguing in Publication Data.
A catalogue record for this book is available from the British Library.

Printed and bound in the UK by TJ International, Padstow, Cornwall

Matador is an imprint of Troubador Publishing Ltd

Author

Rosie Houghton, lives in the South of France with her husband and three children. She was educated in London and after reading Law at Kent University went on to practice as a commercial lawyer in 1992. She was a finalist in the Cosmopolitan Woman of the Year Awards in 2001. She also established her own Internet Company. In 2004, at the age of 36, she retired with her family in France. "Abandoned Love" is Rosie's first novel based on her true story. All the documents referred to in the novel are originals.

TV appearances include, BBC1 World in Action, GMTV, Sky, ITV, Bloomberg, Radio performances, Radio 4, Talk Radio, Five Live and local radio stations.

For Ollie, Zac, Max and Poppy,
With Love.

ROSIE 2007
SOUTH OF FRANCE

N O ONE PREPARED Rosie for that day, the day that changed everything in her life. She often looks back and wonders was it just a dream?

One morning, in late May, she was sitting on her terrace, reading. The sun was beating down and she had just picked up all the leaves that had blown onto the ground. There was a slight breeze rustling through the palm trees, blowing yet more leaves onto the terrace. She couldn't be bothered to pick them up again. She would just have to wait for them to blow into the pool and for the filtration system to pick them up.

Her husband had been in the recording studio all week. She was becoming somewhat of a studio widow these days. Time was sort of passing them by and she thought about her up and coming birthday in September, the inevitable forty. She still hadn't started to make efforts to find her real mother who was Irish even though she wanted to. Of course, she had attempted to "Google" her but always, the inevitable "No Results Found" came up. Her adoptive mother Marjorie was now in her eighties and she just couldn't bear to hurt her feelings whilst she was still alive. Nevertheless time was ticking. She had three children who sooner rather than later would need to know she was adopted.

There was not a cloud in the sky, but it was still not warm enough to go swimming just yet. A large dragonfly, the colour of purple sped across the surface of the water in the swimming pool. It hovered for a millisecond and then flew away again.

About midday she heard the familiar boom of the recording studio door, which meant that her husband was surfacing. He walked through the french windows clearly inspired by something.

"I don't want to bore you with it now," he said pulling at the zip of his jacket, " but I've just done this amazing track and I don't know where the words came from, but I can tell you, it wasn't me writing them."

"What do you mean?" She asked putting her book down and removing her sunglasses.

"I don't know. It sounds like a hymn. The lyrics just wrote themselves. It isn't like anything I've written before. Listen, I've had enough for today. How about we go into the village of Saint Paul, have a walk round the village and maybe get a bite to eat? My legs could do with some stretching."

"Just a minute, whilst I'll grab some things."

She put on some shorts and a shirt and located her shoes underneath the sun bed. Her husband picked up the car keys and the remote for the alarm.

Once they got to Saint Paul, they parked the car behind the post office and started the small descent to the Place Charles de Gaulle, a beautiful square surrounded by plane trees, below where, you can hear the faint clanking of petanque players playing outside the bustling Cafe de Place. Saint Paul has always been a haven for the rich and famous. During the 1960s it was frequented by French actors such as Yves Montand, Simone Signoret and Lino Ventura. They didn't aspire to know who these people were but it is a testament to their notoriety that there are thousands of visitors to this village. The village used to be frequented by many artists such as Chagall and Matisse and indeed many of their works can be seen at the famous restaurant and hotel The Colombe D'Or.

"I know it is a bit early for lunch and I know it is almost impossible to get a table without a reservation, but shall we see if they have got a table?" her husband said as they stood outside the entrance to the hotel on the edge of the square.

They ducked through the arch leading straight through to the terrace adorned with numerous orange and fig trees. All the tables were beautifully laid out with white tablecloths and silver cutlery. A tall man, who they recognised as the headwaiter began to approach them, a serviette draped neatly over his left arm. He was suitably dressed in a black and white uniform.

"Bonjour Monsieur, dame. Comment t'allez-vous?"

They asked if he had a table and the waiter duly scanned the reservations book on the wooden pedestal. They could see from the list that the restaurant was pretty full. They just didn't want to be disappointed now they had mustered up the courage to ask. He picked up a pencil and scribbled on the page.

"Bien Sur!"

He muttered something about this being very unusual but that he did have a table for one o'clock if they wanted to reserve it.

They confirmed they would be back in half an hour after they had made a tour of the village.

They proceeded to climb the cobbled path through the huge vaulted entrance to the village known as the "Porte Royale" and from there onto the old ramparts consisting of tiny old medieval houses leaning against each other, surrounded by an old protective wall of ancient stones. From the top of the fortified wall they could see the shimmering Mediterranean Sea to the South and the snow capped Alps to the North. They hovered in and out of the art galleries, soaking up the contemporary art, a testament to the art lovers who adored this village before them. They walked past a fountain in a courtyard and threw some coins in for good luck. The gentle trickle of the water reminded them of the same fountain they had built in the courtyard of their house. Finally they climbed the steep steps to the Old Cathedral, which rests on the site of a Roman Temple dedicated to Mars and an earlier Mergovingian Church. They entered the confines of the Church just as the sunlight was streaming through the windows, casting a multi coloured hue over the wooden pews. They lit a candle each and said a little prayer as they often did with their children.

They then made their descent back down through the village to the restaurant. On entering the Colombe D'Or they were struck by its' beauty. There were rows of fruit trees to the left and sculptures by Picasso snuggled in the alcoves. The table they showed them to, was in the middle of the restaurant. Rosie placed their dog underneath the table and tied her to the chair. Whilst sitting down, they ordered two "aperitifs" and started to pour over the over sized artistic menus.

The restaurant was packed as usual. They could hear the clink of the water glasses as they were removed and replaced on to the tables. There was a general hum of conversation from the other tables, which gradually got more animated as the restaurant began to fill up. The waiters would keep passing by with food orders and then they would set up a table for carving and serving. Numerous "Pannier crudites" for which the restaurant was famous for, passed by their tables consisting of a huge basket of vegetables with an assortment of charcuterie and anchovy paste.

"I know it's not expensive but I think I'll have the poussin." Rosie said.

"Me too."

The waiter took their order for the food and a bottle of Sancerre. The bread arrived and they each took a piece and carried on talking about their eldest going to Public School in England and how they would cope as a family without him. They didn't really want him to go but he had managed to achieve a scholarship.

" I've booked the flights to go to London in the next few weeks." She said. "I think it may be the time to tell him that I am adopted, you know whilst we just have each other for company. He must suspect something. I mean he must have noticed that I am nothing like Grandma Marjorie."

" Just tell him gently. You know he has quite a tough exam the next day."

" I know. But whilst I am letting him try the entrance for this school as well, I know his heart is set on the Public School you went to."

" It's the costs that are scaring me. At least with the scholarship the school will bear some of the burden." Her husband said taking another sip of his wine.

The conversation flowed easily after a few glasses. They discussed whether they would think about moving back to England. They talked about their friends and their children's friends, drinking in the atmosphere of the Colombe D'Or as so many people had done before them. The food arrived and they carried on talking. The laughter could be heard ascending around them as more bottles were ordered.

By the time their plates had been taken away and the dessert menus placed in front of them, Rosie noticed that some of the diners were drawing their lunches to a close. She couldn't remember what got them talking to the couple next to them. They had a tiny little baby who kept smiling at them. The mother glanced in her direction and they both smiled.

"That's a gorgeous little baby you've got there. She has been well behaved. How old is she?"

"Oh she's three months now. Luckily she sleeps most of the time, although we haven't been getting much sleep these days." She replied with a hint of an Irish accent.

"I know. We've got three children. They are all at school at the moment." Rosie said.

"Oh you live here do you? I should have realised with the cute dog."

"Yes. We've been here for three years now. It's been hard, but the children love it here, and you can't complain about the weather."

"We came to Saint Paul for the art shops," the husband said also with an Irish lilt. "We own an art shop in Dublin."

"Oh you must go and look at a painting we just saw in the village in an art gallery on the left. You can't miss it. The colours are beautiful. We would have bought it ourselves, but we already have enough art at the moment. I've always fancied being an art dealer. I met this art dealer in the Cotswolds. He had amassed thousands of paintings but couldn't bear to sell any of them." Rosie said.

"Do you fancy having a drink with us? My name is Fidelma and this is my husband Nick."

"Yes we would love to. We don't have to pick up the children until 4 o'clock from the bus stop."

Fidelma ordered another bottle of Sancerre.

"What's it like living in France then?"

"Well if you accept that the entire country are out to lunch every day and that nothing gets done, then you will be alright," said Rosie's husband. "We've just been doing a house up and what should have taken 3 months has taken 3 years. Looks like the property market has gone up though so we should be alright even if it has cost a small fortune."

"Don't tell us. The property market in Ireland has been going bonkers. They've knocked down all the old properties in favour of new developments. My brother is a property developer and over the years he has made a mint buying up land and selling it on with planning permission."

"Did you know that many of the famous artists of the twentieth century used to pay for their rooms here by donating their art for free? Have you seen the Renoirs and Picassos in the dining room?" Rosie asked.

"No we shall have to take a look when we leave," said Fidelma.

They carried on talking and sipping their wine. Most of the diners had left the restaurant, so they ordered some coffees and digestives on the house. Something was nagging Rosie to ask the question. They were Irish. She had always known that her real mother was Irish as her adoptive mother had handed her a letter when she was old enough to understand that she was adopted and that the adoption had been arranged privately. She had been given the barest details in that letter but had never been brave enough to go in search of her birth mother even though she desperately wanted to. She had met Irish people before and had never asked the question as to whether anyone knew her mother. Maybe it was the baby, or the Colombe D'Or or the fact she was going to turn forty that year.

"Whereabouts in Ireland do you come from?" She asked.

"Just outside Cork. Why do you ask?"

A silence hung in the air as Rosie caught her husband's eye and then turned back to Fidelma. If she didn't ask this question now she thought, then she will never get this opportunity again. It wasn't as if they were going to see them again? Something was niggling her to ask them the question.

"I know this may sound like a stupid question and I have never asked anybody this before and I know we have only just met, but I am adopted and because I was a private adoption I know the names of my real parents. This is surely a long shot but I've been told by my adoptive mother that my real mother was from Cork and had an unusual surname."

At that moment she paused and saw Fidelma lifting out her baby from the pram and rest her on her knee. She started to bounce her gently up and down causing the baby to smile.

"What was her name?" she asked.

"Miriam Sullivan-Cody."

Fidelma momentarily stopped bouncing her baby and looked towards Nick. She then slowly turned her head back towards Rosie with her mouth slightly ajar.

"Oh my God!" she spluttered "I don't know her but I think my mother might. She's a designer I think."

Her husband went white as a sheet. Rosie was in shock. How could this have happened?

"Listen," Fidelma said pulling out her mobile. "I will try and phone my mother now. She is on her way to the airport and may have her phone switched off but it is worth a try," and with that Fidelma was punching the keys in to her phone. Rosie grabbed her husband's hand and held it tightly. Fidelma held the portable to her ear and after five minutes or so started to shake her head.

"I can't get hold of her."

It was getting close to four o'clock and most of the diners had left the restaurant. The waiters were now pacing around anxiously, waiting for them to leave.

"Listen, I will give you my card and let me take down your number. I will call you the moment I hear anything. I've got a good feeling about this, but I need to speak to my mum. We'll help you find your real mum."

With that they exchanged hugs and kisses and said their goodbyes. When they got back to the house in Saint Paul they were still in shock. Her husband leapt down to the studio and produced the lyrics to the song.

The song had a beautiful ethereal quality to it.

> *Peace On Earth*
> *The message I bring you is peace to you all*
> *I hope your heart will find the way*

She looked out on to the immaculate garden and pondered whether Fidelma would give her the answers she was looking for. She prayed that night that she would.

MIRIAM 1965
DUBLIN

MIRIAM THREW HERSELF down on the long, hardened oak bench in the corner of the crowded pub called O'Neill's in Dublin. It was Friday night and all the usual crowd were there from Cork. David who had just landed a job working for the Dublin Royal Ballet, Humphrey and Pat her best friends from Macroom who had just started a catering business and of course the usual crew over from London. The room was filled with cigarette smoke. The conversations were flowing, getting louder and louder with each round of drinks ordered. The jukebox was blasting with the Beach Boys "I'm feeling those good vibrations"

Her friends were getting some serious Irish rounds in that evening. They always got together on a Friday night. It was 1965 and the 60s were now in full swing. All the girls were wearing the latest fashion statements, mainly sleek tunics and mini skirts. She loved her clothes then. Her ambition was to become a fashion designer. She had already been told she could make it as a top model by Lucie Clayton's modelling school in London. Humphrey came over with a stack of drinks in his hand and a couple of packets of crisps stuffed in his mouth. He plonked them on the table.

"I can't fecking believe this place on a Friday night. You can't swing a cat in here. Who's for the Cavern later?" He shouted over the crescendoing voices.

"Will you believe it Pat, he's already talking night clubs when we haven't even started the evening."

Friendship was the real reason they were all together on a Friday, and of course, an opportunity to pick up a date. Many of them had travelled and been to and back from London, but they always returned to their homeland Ireland. This was the place you could really let your hair down, with old friends, cracking jokes and sharing the Irish passion for drinking. When you bought a round you bought everyone a round. Before you knew it you had a line of drinks in front of you, waiting to be demolished.

In London the pubs weren't the same. They were much more staid affairs unless you went to one of the avant-garde pubs in the Kings Road where the drugs scene was starting to make a major impact. It was good to be back and hear the Irish lyrical accents all around her.

"God the things I saw going down in London. I'm so glad we have Ireland to come back to, for a bit of normality."

"That's why they call it the swinging sixties." Humphrey replied. " Buildings and skirts are getting higher, hair longer and the music louder."

At that moment her elder sister walked in wearing a replica Mary Quant black and white checkered short skirt and tailored jacket. Her hair hung loosely round her shoulders, protected by a loose headscarf.

"Hi sis, how are you doing?"

"Oh for the love of God I need a drink. Those frigging buses are never on time. I got absolutely soaked. It's raining cats and dogs out there!"

Miriam slowly lit a cigarette and inhaled its' contents. The bar had the smell of drink loitering in the air as people pushed past spilling their pints. It was good to be back. She had spent the last three months at St Martin's Lane College of Art and Design in London. The course was the same her father had done many years back. There weren't very many women on the course, but that wasn't unusual in those days when more women went in to modelling or became air hostesses. She wanted to do more with her life, to become successful in her own right. London had taught her the new meaning of ambition. She had seen sweeping changes in the fashion industry which had previously been aimed at the wealthy and elite only to be replaced by a younger group of people eager to buy ready wear fashion off the shelves on the high street. She came from a large family and wanted to break free, free from the reigns of Catholicism which still weighed heavily on them in those days.

"Do you think there will be any peace in Ireland one day or will we always be at each other's fecking throats?"

She didn't want to comment. Her father was English, which posed a real threat to them in Ireland in those days. Her mother was Irish. The only reason they didn't stand out in their community was because they had been brought up in the Jewish community of Cork. This was the quietly ambitious community that just kept their heads down and concentrated on hard work and making money. Many unbeknown to her were to go on and be famous designers.

"So how's the new job with the ballet? What do you get to do?" She asked David.

"Oh I get to choreograph all the male dancers, which is fun! Nothing like the sight of a male dancer in tight leggings."

"David, that is too much information, you naughty boy."

"You never know you might get a peak yourself, if you succeed. I might be able to tip some fashion design your way, when you're established. It beats having to slog away at a factory all day."

He looked at the others, then turned and gave her one of his classic cheeky grins. David was as camp and gay as the best of them and she loved him for it. None of them asked where he hung out when he was not with them or how many lovers he had, but they knew that if you were in the theatre or ballet that you were probably likely to encounter a strong gay fraternity.

"So, how's your love life Miriam?"

"Oh I don't have any one special at the moment."

"Didn't meet anyone special in London then?"

"No, no one special," she replied somewhat wistfully. She gently stroked the stem of her glass, savouring her surroundings.

"All you need is love." came rolling out on the Juke Box.

"Anyone want another drink?" David asked.

"I'll get these in." Miriam said. "It's my turn."

She got up and straightened her skirt. She popped to the Ladies through the sea of people and retouched her make up and applied some hairspray to her newly cut bob. As she pouted her lips and showered herself with Chanel No 5, she took another look at her reflection in the mirror. Not bad for a model if she said so herself. She edged through the heaving crowds towards the bar. She could feel the admiring glances from all the men in the room as she walked past. She knew most eyes were trying to catch her attention, for any response that might acknowledge their existence or give them an indication as to whether their attraction was reciprocated.

One man's glance at the bar opposite trapped her attention. He was older than her, dressed in a smart suit with an air of superiority about him. He was chatting to a group of men of similar stature. His blond hair was swept back and his blue eyes kept smiling at her, mesmerizing her. He was laughing and joking with his friends, yet kept glancing in her direction. His skin was slightly suntanned, as if he had just come back from holiday. He seemed to be commanding the attention of his friends, clearly in control of the conversation. He wasn't flirting with her, he was too far away, but he was just looking at her in between talking and laughing with his friends. There didn't seem to be a female companion with him. Don't what ever you do make it look obvious that you fancy him, she told herself. Just calmly order the drinks and return to your friends. She locked out of his eye embrace and took the drinks back to the table.

"What took you so long sis? You were ages."

"Oh there was a queue at the bar. You know what it is like trying to push yourself past all those men."

The conversation continued to flow but she wasn't listening. The way that man had glanced at her had disarmed her. How would she attract his attention without him knowing? She couldn't go up to the bar again, that would be too obvious. She didn't want to leave for the night club in case he didn't come. In any event it probably wasn't his scene. He looked far too sophisticated to want to go to the Cavern. Maybe if she went to the Ladies, she would catch a glimpse of him again.

"Sis you haven't been listening to a word I have been saying, have you?"

"Oh sorry, I was in a different world."

"It's not something you're not telling me?"

"No, no, nothing like that."

She could hear the laughter getting louder and louder from his side of the bar, but couldn't see him. From the sound of their high clipped accents, they weren't Irish. She tried to ogle the conversation, but the bar was so busy and noisy, it was impossible to catch anything.

After what seemed like an infinite period of time, she caught him walking towards her in the direction of the Mens toilets. As he glided effortlessly through the crowds, she could not avert his gaze.

"Len, I thought it was you! How are you doing?" cried her friend Pat. She got up to give him two air kisses. Oh my God she knew him. Miriam tried to fain nonchalance but he turned round and looked at her.

"So these are your friends, I take it."

"Yes, let me introduce you. Humphrey, David, Orla and her sister Miriam. "

He duly walked round and shook their hands.

"We are all going to the Cavern later if you want to join us?"

"I might just do that," he said. "I'm still a bit jet lagged though. I've only just got back from South Africa."

"The girls mentioned that you were off on another speculative investment."

"We still had time to pack in some Game Reserves. Listen I've got some business to finish up with at the bar. I might catch you guys later."

And with that he continued in the direction of the Mens. She had no idea whether he would make it to the club or whether she would ever see him again. She did not know if the others had noticed the warm mutual attraction between them.

"How do you know him?" she asked.

"Oh he has been in all the Society pages. Quite a scandal. He was married to Lady O'Connell and got divorced last year. He is a hugely successful businessman in his own right. We used to live close to his family, before he started moving in those circles. I think he spends a lot of time in South Africa. I always thought he was a bit of a catch, until this O'Connell scandal. I think his ex wife got remarried pretty quickly and the new husband adopted his children."

" Children?" she asked.

"Well he is about fifteen years older than us."

"How terrible to lose your children."

"I don't know why. It could be that is the only way they could get citizenship to South Africa."

Even though this was the 1960s divorce was still considered a shameful thing in the eyes of Catholicism, that and children out of wedlock.

Miriam still had about four rounds of drinks to get through, but she didn't want to be drunk when she next saw him, if he did turn up at the club. She briefly saw his back when he returned from the Mens, before it disappeared into the crowd. Now she couldn't see him at all. She strained her neck to see if she could still hear their voices but the noise in the pub had risen to another level.

"What's wrong sis, you're not drinking?"

"You know what? I don't feel like any more. Shall we just go straight to the club? Perhaps after a few dances, I will feel like some more."

"Lets go then."

She quickly scanned the pub again, but there was still no sight of him or his friends

They picked up their belongings and edged through the crowds to the exit. They stumbled out of the swing doors into the cold night air. The rain had stopped thank goodness, so she needn't worry about her hair. Perhaps he had already left and gone straight home she thought. After all he did say he was jet lagged.

There were plenty of revellers in the street teetering in their heels along the pavements. She could hear the splash of the rainwater on the streets from the cars as they went past. The Cavern was only two blocks away, so they decided to walk there. When they arrived at the entrance, two burly blokes were there to greet them and wave them in. She could hear the loud music pulsating from the club below.

There were hardly any people in the club as it was still early. She cast her eye over the dance floor but there was still no sight of him. Her heart sank. Had he decided to call it a night she wondered?

"I'm going to grab us a table and then Miriam it's your turn to get the drinks."

Miriam edged up to the bar which had three champagne buckets full of champagne.

"Let me get these," she heard a voice say behind her with a hint of a South African accent. She could feel his breath on her neck and felt his hand on hers.

"I suspect everyone will be wanting champagne. I'll buy two bottles, then, we can keep one to ourselves. Don't whatever you do, go back to your friends. Just stay here," he said with some authority. "Hi Tina. Can we have two bottles of Bollinger, one for that table over there and one here?"

The waitress went off to get the champagne glasses and two bottles from the fridge. Len grabbed a stool and sat down next to her. She noticed he was on his own.

"Your friends didn't come then?"

"No I sent them packing. I wanted you to myself."

"Cheers!"

"Cheers!"

Miriam took a small sip from her glass and placed it back on the bar. She took a sneak preview over her shoulder to check that her friends were happily ensconced at their table, which they were.

"So, you have just got back from South Africa, I take it?" trying to avoid any awkward silences.

"I have various business interests over there, mainly in property development. I split my time between London, Dublin and Cape Town."

"I've just come back from London."

"What took you there?"

"Oh modelling mainly and a fashion design course. I hope to be a fashion designer one day."

"Not that ambitious then?"

He smiled again, his eyes searching for that hint of reciprocation, which she gave. Her friends were too busy talking to notice that she had not returned. The music was playing, but they didn't notice.

"I tried to stick it out in London, but it's hard to earn enough to get a proper flat."

"It looks like you're a woman used to nice things."

"Oh I like nice clothes, nice things. Doesn't everyone?"

"Good, because you'll enjoy being with me."

"What I love about London is that it is embracing change. No longer is Knightsbridge dominated by the stuffy establishments only prepared to endorse haute couture. There are lots of opportunities for young designers like me." She took another sip of her champagne and grabbed an olive from the tiny bowl on the bar in front of them.

"It seems to me that the whole of society is on the move at the moment. Take what I do which is property development. I see the old order dying, particularly in Ireland. Ireland used to be full of traditionalist values based on rural, religious and nationalist ideologies. But now the Capitalist Market is having an influence. It's a great opportunity to make money if you know the right people."

Miriam pulled out a packet of cigarettes from her bag, listening intently.

"Here, let me" Len said proffering her a light and then lighting his own.

"I think when Kennedy came to visit a few years back he did a lot to raise this country's profile."

"You're not telling me Ireland is now full of rock and roll, space races and smart clothes." Miriam laughed "I can't see Ireland losing its' heart which is Catholicism. I was always taught to believe that a family who pray together, stay together."

"That's where my last marriage must have gone wrong," he replied staring blankly into the distance.

At that point they were interrupted by Pat who was willing them to come and join them. Eager to avoid getting tangled up with the group again she was relieved when Len suggested that perhaps they should dance to the next song.

"Come on," he said stubbing out their cigarettes. " I could do with getting to know you more intimately."

"You know the moment I saw you in that pub I was hooked," he said whilst they danced.

"I guessed as much."

"Listen, I'd love to stay, but I am totally jet lagged. Here's my card with my number on it. Give me a call in the next few days and we'll do lunch. I'll say my goodbyes to the others."

She took his embossed company card, which confirmed he was managing director of some property development company in Dublin. He said his goodbyes to their group and then left.

"What's with you two sis?"

"Oh nothing."

Miriam didn't want to let on that there was more to this, in case nothing happened. They stayed and danced some more before saying their goodbyes that evening. She somehow knew in her heart that her life would never be the same again having met Len.

MARJORIE 1965
LONDON

MARJORIE LEANED AGAINST the sideboard in her kitchen overlooking the neatly manicured gardens below her in London. The wind rustled through the trees, whispering. The traffic was thundering outside with its' normal monotonous drone. Marjorie put the kettle on the stove and waited for it to whistle. Her life was starting to feel better now. She had started a job at the solicitors Trower and Hamlins in New Square. Her position was as legal secretary to one of the leading partners. The offices were situated right near the Law Courts on the Strand and she was looking forward to going and watching some interesting cases after work. The pay was adequate, but she had been assured some overtime if she worked hard. She loved the smell of those offices, of old leather books and glorious mahogany polished wood. Her digs were just around the corner in a small mansion block off Marylebone High Street. In the background she could hear her neighbour switch the radio on to "She loves you ye ye". She didn't have much time for contemporary music then. In any event it was her birthday and she had reached the dreaded age of forty-two. Not good when you are still single. But she liked this new band who she thought was starting to become quite famous, the Beatles. They somehow made you feel upbeat about life.

Things had not always been so good for Marjorie. She grew up in the shadows of the First and Second World Wars and got married to a completely unsuitable guy Anthony in the Second World War, only to be divorced again by the time she was twenty one. At the time she thought this guy in uniform would sweep her off her feet. Little did she know that she would be left with the responsibility of looking after his parents. For many years after that, life just drudged on. How could she have reached forty-two and not done anything with her life?

She poured herself a cup of coffee and slowly sipped its' contents. She didn't have to go to work as it was a Saturday. She contemplated going to the cinema but there was nothing that took her fancy. She picked up a copy of the previous days' Standard and idly flipped through its pages. They were advertising a special offer for the Planetarium at Tussauds, something to do with stars and infinite galaxies. As she had nothing better to do, Marjorie decided to get dressed and take the short walk to Baker Street.

She put on a pale woollen dress with matching shoes and small leather belt. She grabbed a warm winter coat and her clutch bag and applied some make up. When she stepped out in to the High Street, the coldness of the February air burnt her cheeks. The sun was shinning but it was still bitterly cold. She started to walk briskly to get the circulation going in her feet. She could hear her footsteps falling in line with all the other busy shoppers on that Saturday morning, eager to get their last purchases from the winter sales.

She decided that as it was her birthday, she would hail a cab. The Planetarium was not far and it seemed a shame to scuff her shoes getting there.

"Where to luv?" said the taxi driver.

"The Planetarium, Baker Street please." She said.

"That's the popular place next to Madame Tussauds. I wouldn't mind taking the wife there." He replied.

The warm heaters of the taxi blasted out at her bringing a warm glow to her cheeks. The taxi driver narrowly missed a pedestrian as he turned in to Marylebone. As they pulled up outside Madame Tussauds, she could see a large queue snaking round the corner.

"You still want me to drop you off here luv? It looks like you are in for a wait." The taxi driver said.

"Yes thanks. I've got nothing better to do."

"That will be five shillings miss."

She handed him his change for the fare and braved the cold streets of London again. The queue was about half a mile long and you could see that some of the children were getting restless. Funny enough she'd never thought about having children. Life had sort of passed her by between the ages of twenty-one and forty-two. She'd met a few boyfriends along the way but none of them were ready to commit or were already married. It seemed society was becoming more liberal as far as women were concerned, now that the contraceptive pill was becoming freely available.

Marjorie took a place at the end of the queue and waited. After standing still for about twenty minutes she received a tap on the shoulder from the gentleman behind her. He was dressed smartly in a dark blue suit and a cashmere overcoat.

"Excuse me," he said tapping a cigarette on his silver cigarette case. "You wouldn't happen to have a light perhaps?"

She slowly retained her composure whilst she opened her clutch bag and carefully took out a pewter lighter given to her by her parents. She handed it to him and he offered her a cigarette which she accepted. They stood in silence whilst they smoked, unable to come up with anything to say.

"Strange to think this place was built on the site of an old cinema that was destroyed in the Second World War." He remarked.

"I know. It is sort of fitting to be reminded of the universe and how small we all are twenty years on." She replied.

"I thought I'd give this place a bash, see if it is a place my boys would like to go to," he finally conjectured.

"Oh, you are married?" Marjorie replied far too quickly.

"No, divorced actually. Awful predicament. I don't get to see them, you see, except on alternate weekends."

"Oh I'm sorry."

"Don't be."

A silence ensued. She could see his eyes steering towards the wedding finger on her left hand. By now she deduced that he could certainly see she was single. She suddenly blurted out.

"I was married once, more of a shot gun wedding as it transpired. I suppose the war was to blame. I ended up spending more time with my husband's father than my husband."

The queue slowly edged forward. A teacher in front of them was trying to control a bunch of unruly school children. Some were playing with make-shift catapults from elastic bands, throwing bits of chewing gum at the teacher.

"So why, if you don't mind me asking, have you come here by yourself?" he asked hesitantly. "I am sure you are not short of suitors."

"No," she blushed, the crimson etching in on her cheeks. "I'm celebrating."

"What celebrating on your own?"

"Something like that."

Marjorie didn't want to let on to this gentleman that it was her forty-second birthday. It seemed old. She didn't feel any different to when she was seventeen, but somehow being in your forties, unmarried and with no children, seemed like a failure and she didn't want to impart this, just yet, on this chance encounter.

"I can't stand queuing, it seems such a waste of life."

"I know, but the queue seems to be gathering pace now."

At that moment, a porter blew his whistle and ushered them to a second entrance which had just been opened. As they pushed forward, stubbing out their cigarettes, the gentleman put a reassuring hand on her shoulder.

"Listen, I hope you don't think I'm being presumptuous, but I would like to grab a spot of lunch afterwards." He paused as if catching his breath. "That's if you feel like celebrating with a complete stranger."

The crowd was now gathering momentum behind them. She touched his warm cashmere coat, returning his gaze for a second, and said.

"I'd love to."

They entered the building and after paying for their tickets were led by the attendant to a large auditorium. The place was pitch dark and Marjorie clung onto the gentleman's arm as they edged towards their seats on the front row. They had to strain their necks to look up at the huge hemispherical ceiling illuminating the 360 degrees night sky.

"I'm a little nervous." She said.

"You shouldn't be. I think the whole experience is meant to be one of wonderment."

The forty-five minute show started with a series of constellations, lighting up before the audience. There were gasps as a myriad of glimmering lights lit up the roof to the booming voice of the narrator informing them about the universe.

"You know there are a billion galaxies up there," the gentleman whispered in to her ear.

"I know. It makes us feel so insignificant." She replied.

When the show finally finished, they slowly walked with the rest of the crowd to the exit. Marjorie had to shield her eyes from the brightness of the daylight as they hit the pavement.

"You forget it is still daytime when you're inside there." She remarked.

"It reminds me of coming out of the cinema."

"I don't even know your name." She said.

"Arthur."

They grabbed a cab and set off to his favorite French restaurant in Leicester Square. Whilst he paid the taxi driver Marjorie stood outside the discreet entrance with a canopy inscribed with the name of the restaurant "L'Escargot". He held her hand as they ascended the steps to a small dark room filled with waiters dressed head to toe in black and white.

They showed them to a small table in the corner, by the window, overlooking the busy theatregoers below.

"It's a shame it's February, otherwise I would have taken you out on the terrace. You can just about see the National Gallery and St Martin's church from the roof top."

"Oh this is just perfect." She replied.

The waiters took their coats and they sat down at the table. They ordered two gin and tonics. As the drinks fizzed around the chunky ice cubes, they clinked their glasses.

"You never told me what we are celebrating?" He smiled.

"My birthday."

"Happy Birthday." He beamed. "I won't ask you your age if you won't ask mine. I suspect I am considerably older, though not wiser than you in years. In any event, I wouldn't want to appear rude."

"Thanks."

Marjorie had snails for the first time and he ordered a very expensive bottle of wine.

"So why the Planetarium?" He asked.

"Oh, I don't know," she said twisting her tiny silver fork between her fingers. "I'm looking forward to seeing that new David Lean film, Doctor Zhivago, but it isn't out in the cinemas yet."

"Isn't that based on Boris Pasternak's novel about a protagonist, Yuri Zhivago, a medical doctor who is torn between two women, during the Russian revolution?"

"You're very knowledgeable."

"Comes with the territory, I'm afraid, when you've been Public School educated, like me. Not that I enjoyed the experience."

"Did you enjoy University?" She asked.

"Loved it. I was at Trinity College, Cambridge."

"I wish I'd been to University. The war got in the way of that."

"Where would you have gone?"

"Oh I had a place at the Sorbonne in Paris." Marjorie said ruefully. If truth be known she would have loved to have gone there.

"Sometimes life is not so kind to us. At least we both came out of the war unscathed. I was too old for service."

"I know I lost many friends, in the air force who were shot down. It doesn't bear thinking about."

The waiter came past and removed their plates. He proceeded to pour them some more wine.

"Do you think that like the stars that we saw in the show, that is what happens when we die?" asked Marjorie, smoothing down her napkin. "I often wonder about servicemen during the war, what happened to them."

"There are some who believe that when your time has come it has come."

"I don't know. It seems so unfair. My best friend in the WRENS was shot down in a Lancaster bomber over the Channel. I can't imagine how awful her last minutes must have been, drowning."

"I think that looking at the stars can offer us some comfort."

They were the last to leave the restaurant that day.

"Thank you for buying me lunch." Marjorie said, letting Arthur put on her overcoat.

"The pleasure was mine I can assure you. I don't know if you've had enough of me yet, but do you fancy taking a walk through the parks? It's still light and I fancy working off lunch if you are up for it."

"I'd love to." She replied.

They took a stroll through Leicester Square and then down Piccadilly to Green Park. They both remarked on how vibrant London had now become. They passed through the heaving crowds of shoppers and narrowly missed cyclists as they ran across red traffic lights. As the light began to fade, they marvelled at the brightly lit billboards adorning the streets. The city had moved on since the war and was now full of young people again. It may have been Marjorie's forty-second birthday but she didn't feel it in this environment. She hadn't had so much fun for awhile. The shops were full of the new spring collections. It was hard to think that spring would be coming soon on that cold February day. They stopped off at Fortnum and Masons and browsed round the food store. They bought a small box of chocolates and a tin of Fortnum's biscuits, just to say they'd been there.

Finally when they were too tired to talk any more he ordered her a cab home.

"I will be able to see you again won't I?"

Marjorie reached down in her bag for a small card with her details on it.

"Thanks for a lovely day," she replied, handing him her details.

He gently stroked her cheek with one finger and then blew her a kiss.

"Until next time."

And with that the taxi drove off. She didn't dare look back, in case she appeared too eager. She knew without a doubt she wanted to see this man again.

MIRIAM 1965
DUBLIN

THE NEXT MORNING Miriam awoke at her sister's flat. Her boyfriend had not turned up last night as promised and she was fuming.

"Why are men such bastards, sis? He could have phoned or something. He just keeps me hanging on the whole time."

Miriam was nursing a cup of coffee, reminiscing about last night's events. She took out the card he had given her from her bag. Should she phone him or would that look too eager? She hadn't given him her number so he couldn't phone her, but maybe he could get her number from Pat and Humphrey as they appeared to know him. She was meant to be starting a new job next week, with Brown Thomas in fashion. She couldn't afford to be distracted with a new love in her life. Yet her heart ached to see him again. Caution advised her that this man had baggage. He had been married before and had children. Was it right to get involved with an older man? Would he ever commit if things got serious? What would happen if she found herself falling in love with this guy? She put all such thoughts to the back of her mind for fearing the answers.

"So are you going to give this guy Len a call then?"

"What do you mean?"

"Well I saw him give you his card last night. He must want to see you again?"

"I don't want to appear too keen."

"Oh, so it is serious then?"

"Maybe."

"Well don't let him treat you the way my Patrick treats me. You deserve more than that sis."

Miriam drained her cup of coffee and put it on the sideboard next to the sink. It was another dull day outside in Dublin. The streets were grey and the skies were heavy with rain. This was her last weekend, before she was due to start her job next week. The pay was going to be good and she was excited at the opportunity it was going to give her. Both her sister and her wanted to gain some work experience before setting up their own company in fashion design. Her sister was good with her hands and a great seamstress. All they needed was a lucky break in the Industry. Brown Thomas was one of the leading dress companies in Dublin at the time. It was right in the centre of Dublin next to the Grand Hotel. Her sister's apartment was only a stones throw from the centre.

Miriam's sister had been dating Patrick for about six months now and it was getting quite serious. She hadn't introduced him to their parents, but they knew of him. They were still in their early twenties and whilst they didn't want to settle down just yet, knew that their parents would only ever approve of a long term relationship if it was heading for marriage. Ireland was staunchly Catholic in those days. Her father had converted to Catholicism after marrying their mother and they were all brought up to be strict Catholics. They went to

Church every Sunday and said their Hail Mary's. They had attended a formal Catholic School in Macroom.

"What shall we do today?"

"I fancy a bit of shopping."

"You not going to phone him then?"

"Not today. Anyway he has given me his work number so I guess I won't until next week sometime."

That weekend Miriam couldn't stop thinking about him. Thoughts of their chance encounter consumed her mind. They passed through store after store often trailing the men's departments before entering the ladies. She spied suits that she thought he would buy or wear. She bought a few dresses that she knew would look good on her if she next saw him. The stores were heaving that day with people looking for the latest trendy garments. Christmas was only three months away and some people were starting their Christmas shopping early. The shops weren't decked out with Christmas decorations just yet, but the feel of winter approaching had begun. Miriam needed to shop to distract her thoughts of him. Was he thinking about her like she was thinking about him? When would he have to go back to South Africa? How was she going to cope with a long distance relationship if they ended up having one?

"I'm exhausted. Shall we go for a drink?"

And so they made their way to the pub that they had been to the night before, but there was no sign of him there that evening. Maybe he was still jet lagged, or maybe he was out on the town with some mates or maybe he was dining with some woman somewhere in a fancy restaurant? She couldn't bear the thought of him being with someone else.

"Are you seeing Patrick tonight? Miriam asked.

"I gave him such a bollocking for last night. He's making it up to me by taking me to the cinema, a Julie Christie movie, I think. What have you planned?"

"Oh I'll probably give David a call, see if he is up for an after theatre drink. He likes that bar where all the gays hang out. I think I'll be safe there."

After a couple of drinks they said their goodbyes and headed their separate ways into the night. David and Miriam had this routine on a Saturday of meeting up with a few of his friends after the ballet. The bar was tucked in a tiny alleyway behind the theatre. Its' outer windows bowed out like a ship with the warm lights willing you inside. The ceilings were low and you had to duck slightly so as not to bang your head. The pub was full of theatrical types exclaiming "Darling how are you?" The voices were so loud and affected, it felt like you were in the theatre. Miriam spied David animatedly talking to some of his darlings in the corner and drew up a stool next to him.

"Hello gorgeous, how's my favorite queenie? I've bought you a glass of wine already. I want to hear all the goss."

"There is no goss David!" she said slapping his knee. He let out one of those belly aching laughs, then swigged his pint and whispered in her ear. "You forget my darling, I saw you with him last night. There are quite a few tongues wagging, I can assure you."

"He gave me his card. So what!"

"You'd better play hard to get with that one. He has quite a reputation with the ladies."

"Don't ruin this one for me David."

"You're quite smitten. I can tell."

"Nothing happened."

"Oh it will."

The noise levels got louder and louder. More people were now piling out of the theatre, desperate to get to the bar for last orders. Sometimes these pubs had "lock ins" but this was at the discretion of the Landlord. Guys were openly hugging each other with wanton abandon celebrating their last performance on stage that evening. Many were still in their ballet costumes and covered in make-up, gesticulating with their arms in a theatrical manner. Miriam loved being part of this crowd. They would always flirt with you but they never felt a threat to you, because you knew they only had eyes for their own. Women interested them, to be emulated, revered even adored, but not to take home with them. She felt safe in this world, away from the world of real men. If Len was anything to go by, real men threatened her, threatened to take away the one true feeling left, of love. Had she fallen for this man or was it just a dream? She wanted to see him again, but was frightened of the consequences. No one had affected her like this. She was aching to see him again.

The following morning she was due to start work at Brown Thomas in the centre of Dublin. She had carefully chosen what to wear that morning, a chic black tunic and some patent shoes with a silk scarf wrapped around her head to keep her bob in place. The walk to the store wasn't far and the day was surprisingly sunny. The trees had turned to a wintry shade of grey and silver. The leaves had not fallen yet. That would happen when the winds came. Miriam kept thinking of Len and whether she should phone him. She still had his card, in her bag.

"Today we will be initiating you on the shop floor. The most important thing to remember girls is that you are there to serve the customer. You must compliment them at all times. Politeness will be expected of you at Brown Thomas."

To be honest, Miriam didn't really want to start on the shop floor, but you had to start somewhere. In some ways, she felt the shop floor was beneath her, but if she was to climb up the ladder, she had to make a lasting impression to the management. That is why she had taken such pride in her appearance that morning. That and of course Len. Working at Brown Thomas was equivalent to working in Harrods in London in those days. The building was imposing with two footmen at the door. The clothes were expensive and would be worn by the wealthy in Dublin. The store was immaculate with lines of brass counters equipped with measurers and cutters. There were made to measure suits and ready wear items, neatly stacked next to each other. The store smelt of exquisite clothes and fabrics.

"Miriam, I propose that you start in the menswear department. You will find that a good place to start, particularly in the made-to-measure section. If you follow the guidance of your mentor, Mrs O'Grady, you will learn the essentials of the trade."

She was introduced to Mrs O'Grady who was an elderly lady, she guessed in her late fifties, who had long grey hair scraped in a bun. She was dressed in tweeds and had a small badge on her jacket lapel which said her name and roll as supervisor.

"Miriam, may I introduce myself and take you to the men's department."

They duly marched off in quick step to the men's department. All the men's heads turned as they entered the room, many casting their eye on the new girl, Miriam. Most of the glances she got were appreciative and she returned them with a smile. Some she thought even David would approve of. Maybe she should suggest he comes in and sees her at the shop when he is next about, or maybe not? Mrs O Grady showed her all the fabrics and which materials should be used for which suit. She explained the measuring table to her and where to keep the pins and fasteners. She then explained how to fill out an order in the order book and how to use the till. She explained that Miriam's hours would be strictly nine to five with an hour for lunch. She was to be punctual and prompt in all things at all times.

To start off with, she found dealing with customers difficult. Each request was individual and bespoke to that particular client. Some would be in a hurry and want to be sold something straight away. Others would take time to choose their fabrics and colours to measure up a tailored suit. She enjoyed serving the customers who wanted to be involved in the design more than the ones who just wanted one off the shelf. You could often make suggestions as to the width of the leg or the length of the jacket.

"I would like something a little more modern than traditional."

Even the Beatles, who were becoming superstars at this time, were seen wearing suits. People wanted designer suits like them. They would often bring in pictures of them, demanding the latest look. The orders would be placed and the customer told to expect the suit ready within the next week or so. Once they had ordered their suit Miriam would help them with their ties and suggest some suitable shoes to go with the suit. Mrs O'Grady was always happy when she persuaded a client to buy the whole ensemble. Over the ensuing days in that first week she quickly got the hang of serving customers and started to enjoy herself. She made sure that every day she dressed immaculately and dealt with customers politely.

During that week Miriam would be tired and exhausted in the evenings. She would often get out her own sketch pad and draw her own ideas. She would come up with all sorts of designs not just for men's clothes, but for women's clothes as well. She would spend hours doodling sketches.

"Why haven't you phoned him sis?" her sister said one evening.

"Oh I don't know. It is something David said. I don't want to be seen chasing him."

But she was dying to ring Len, dying to meet him again. All through the days she couldn't stop thinking about him, how she might bump in to him on the street or see him again at the bar. Something inside her told her not to pick up the phone in case he was seeing somebody.

That Friday, Miriam was in the shop as usual, tidying up the order book, ready to go off duty. Mrs O'Grady was taking the day's takings to the back of the store and the boys were folding up and tidying away the various fabrics.

"Have you been avoiding me?" A man's voice said in that South African accent. She looked up and saw his beautiful eyes smiling at her, the eyes that had grabbed her across the bar the week before.

"How did you find me? How did you know I worked here?"

"Well, you didn't call me, so I had to ring Pat and find out where you were. She told me you had just started here."

Mrs O'Grady started to walk back in to the room. Miriam's heart leapt a beat. "Shssh," she whispered. "My boss is coming back! You'll have to pretend you're buying something."

"What do you sell?"

"Anything."

"Are you for sale?"

"No!" she said with a hint of a giggle in her voice.

"Miriam! Is this gentleman being served?"

"Yes ma'am."

"Sir, I can show you our extensive range of ties, if you would care to come this way."

Mrs O'Grady looked at Miriam a little suspiciously. Normally she would be selling a customer the full range of options, the tie, being the last one of them. It was the only section where she could get Len out of earshot.

"I'll buy a tie if you say you'll come out with me tonight." He whispered. "I'll be around the corner at O'Neills waiting for you." He added.

She nodded and with his eyes still smiling at her, she took a tie to the counter and he paid for it. He then winked at her and left.

"That man looked far too expensive to just be wanting to buy a tie!" exclaimed Mrs O'Grady.

"I'm sure he will be back." Miriam smiled.

"I just don't get you Miriam sometimes."

With that they closed up the department. Miriam put on her coat, re-touched her make up and grabbed her bag. The night air was cold when she stepped outside and made her start to shiver. The street lamps let out a faint glow shining on the puddles in the streets. It must have rained earlier on, but now it had stopped leaving the street fresh from the showers. Len was waiting for her outside O'Neill, his suited demeanour looking slightly out of place outside the pub. When they got close, their faces inches from each other, he bent down and kissed her.

"I should have kissed you last time I saw you." He said.

"I know."

"And look at the tie you made me buy! It's bright orange. I'll never wear it. It gives me an excuse to come back to the store and return it." They both collapsed into giggles.

"My boss won't forgive me for not selling you a suit, never mind a returned tie. You can't do that to me."

"Let me take you somewhere for dinner. There's a great place called O'Sheas just round the corner. It won't be noisy in there and at least we won't be distracted."

He took Miriam to a restaurant which was just around the corner in Sheep Street. It was an intimate restaurant lowly lit with several small tables covered with white table cloths and candles.

"Good evening Mr Jackson. You have a reservation I believe?"

"How did you know I would come? Or did you have someone else in mind?"

"I knew you would want watering and feeding." He said. Miriam nudged him in the ribs.

"I'm not some piece of cattle you know. I was a Lucie Clayton model."

The waiter led them to their table. There were a few people who recognized him as they passed their tables. Len said his hellos and then they sat down at their table in the corner. He ordered an expensive bottle of champagne and then stroked her fingers. His suit was beautifully tailored, a pale blue cotton shirt with a thin navy silk jacket, both of which brought out the blue in his eyes which gently danced in the candle light. Len ordered the food. Miriam couldn't decide what to eat on the menu. It all seemed beautifully expensive.

"I'm glad we met that night. Did you stay long after I left?"

"Only long enough to see if my sister's boyfriend would turn up."

They talked about Miriam's plans to become a fashion designer, how she had already learnt some of the tricks of the trade by working at Browns, how she had managed to put some of her own input in to the designing of the suits. She also told him about the drawings she had done and the inspiration for those drawings. He gave her some advice on how to set up a business, what areas of the fashion industry he had been involved in and where it was so easy to go wrong.

"The most important thing is to retain the loyalty of your staff," he said stroking the rim of his glass. "If they like you, they will like working for you. I don't see that being a problem in your case." He smiled slowly.

Miriam asked about his work and he said he was passionate about what he did. At the moment he was working on a number of property developments in Ireland and South Africa. He flipped between his locations in South Africa, London and Dublin. For the near future he planned to stay in Dublin for a while although he did need to go back to South Africa to see his two daughters. She asked him how painful it was to leave his daughters behind, and he said "very". They had had to change their surnames to his ex wife's new husband's, so they could get citizenship in South Africa.

They didn't touch their food that evening. Some of the others, cast intriguing glances their way. They were locked in to each other oblivious to those around them. As the evening drew to a close, Len asked to settle the bill. They then put their coats on and made for the door.

"Goodnight sir"

Outside they wrapped themselves together.

"I'd like to see you again, Miriam."

"Me too."

"Listen, give me your number and I'll call you."

Miriam scribbled her number on a piece of paper. He then hailed her a cab home. She still knew that they had something special. She was smiling broadly as she took that taxi home.

MARJORIE 1965
LONDON

MARJORIE DIDN'T HAVE to wait long for Arthur to phone her after their chance meeting at the Planetarium. She was sitting in her offices at Trower and Hamlins in New Square just off Middle Temple when the phone rang.

"I have a gentleman on line one for you Marjorie. He says it's personal."

She checked to see that Mr Maitland, her boss was otherwise engaged and then pressed the extension.

"How is my birthday girl then?"

"Oh so, so." She said with a smile. Marjorie was glad he had called. She had been worried that he thought she had been quite forward agreeing to go with him to lunch that day, despite hardly knowing him. She knew that she had met a potential soul mate, as she hadn't stopped thinking about him since they last met.

"Listen, I can't speak for long," he said with some urgency, "As I am really busy at the moment, but do you fancy meeting for a drink after work?"

Marjorie glanced over at her boss again who was now riffling through some papers, clearly having mislaid something. She knew he would come marching in to her offices barking some orders, if he couldn't find it. She quickly responded.

"Yes I'd love to."

"How about we meet in your neck of the woods. You work in the Temple, am I right in assuming?"

"Yes," she replied still eyeing Mr Maitland. "But can we meet somewhere more non local. I mean most of my bosses grab a quick swifter round here before going home?"

"OK, I get the drift. Lets meet at Hampstead tube station and we can go for a drink at the Flask, say 7 o'clock?"

"See you then." Marjorie clicked the phone down just in time to hear the buzzer calling her into the office. She stood up quickly and straightened her skirt, then grabbed a note pad and pen. Mr Maitland in the short time she had been there, nearly always needed to dictate some shorthand to her. It was always wise to go in prepared.

The rest of the day passed in a haze. Various assistants would pop in to her offices asking for small jobs to be done. The phone would ring intermittently, often calls from clerks at chambers, asking her to confirm details of conferences with counsel. She would then check that the instructions to counsel had been sent out and that a copy had been retained for that meeting. The documents were neatly stacked on her table with swathes of red ribbon round them.

That evening she tidied up her desk and covered her typewriter, making sure she had enough ink for the following day. She also blotted her blotting pad. As she left the offices, she checked her tube map. Her nearest tube station was Inner Temple, so she took the walk, across Middle Temple Lane and into Fountain Court. There were various barristers mingling around, no doubt discussing the events of the day. It was too cold to keep still for long. The street lamps cast a lovely glow over the old stone buildings. When she got to the underground there were crowds of commuters anxious to get home after work. She dashed down the escalators into the warmth of the station. There was a slow hum before the roar of the underground train as it hit the station.

When Marjorie got to Hampstead, Arthur was standing outside in his thick winter overcoat. He had a cashmere scarf tied around his neck and was clutching his brief case.

"Hello stranger."

He then put his arms around her shoulders and they walked with ease over Hampstead Heath towards Highgate. The Heath was quieter in the night air compared to the hustle of Central London. She could hear her footsteps falling into time with his own.

"I like to get out of London." he said, lighting a cigarette "I've got a place in Barnet. It's a bit of a commute."

"I know what you mean, London can be a bit claustrophobic. I love it though. I originally, came from Yorkshire. There was nothing to do there."

"Snap! My family are from Cheshire, from a long line of Ronsons. We've all somehow ended up here though."

As they approached the Flask, you could see the place was packed, through the leaded windows. Arthur opened the door and ushered Marjorie to a table in the corner by the fireplace which was crackling away with some new thrown logs on it. Arthur went to the bar and ordered them some drinks.

"I've taken the liberty of ordering us two shepherd's pies. They are really good here.'

He said placing the drinks on the table. He slowly removed his coat and scarf and placed them on the clotheshorse behind him. The pub was crowded yet cosy and warm.

"That sounds perfect, particularly on a cold winter's night like tonight."

"I hope you don't mind me asking," he said offering her a cigarette " Have you been single for long?"

"I won't answer that question unless you answer it first." She said smiling.

"Well I've been single for too long," he paused, as if trying to gauge her reaction. "Do you think we can work? I'm afraid I come with baggage."

The fact that he had two sons and had been married before didn't phase Marjorie and in many ways made him more beguiling to her.

"Do you think people are destined to be together?" Marjorie said, allowing Arthur to light the cigarette he had given her. Arthur took a sip of his pint and licked the foam from his lips.

"I think if an opportunity arises, and you don't take it, then you can't blame yourself later, if things don't work out for you. In life you are given various olive branches, and you have to take them."

"I remember going to Italy when I was younger and they have a different attitude to life, as if they live life for the moment." Marjorie said. She could feel the warmth of the fire start to warm her fingers and decided to take her jacket off.

"Us English are quite cool and reserved. It holds us back in a number of ways, which means sometimes we miss these opportunities.

It doesn't always mean we end up with the right person, it just means that when the right person comes along, we may well miss them without realizing it. Similarly, we could grab an opportunity which was the wrong opportunity, and forever regret in our lives that we were shackled with responsibility with the wrong person, if you understand my reasoning."

Marjorie continued to listen, the alcohol was clearly helping to relax him.

"So sometimes, following your heart can be a mistake. Not always, but your heart needs to be in the right place when you are following it. In other words you need to be happy in your own soul to be able to hold on and join with another. I know it sounds deep, but we lead such short lives, we only have one chance of getting it right."

Arthur paused as the barmaid brought their shepherd's pies to the table. The steam was still rising from the mash potato topping. She laid down two sets of knives and forks for them wrapped in two serviettes. Arthur opened his and placed it on his lap.

"So many people get it wrong, maybe that is why there are so many sinners in the world. Who knows it may be the basis of the Christian religion."

"You mean forgive us this day for our daily trespasses as we forgive those who trespass against us?" She responded.

"Exactly." He said, picking up his fork and diving into the pie.

"But you can't forgive the big sins, I mean the Church can't exonerate everything."

"No, but it helps us feel better about ourselves particularly if you are Catholic." He said taking his first mouthful.

"I've always liked the Catholic religion. It seems to me far more serious and authentic. I don't agree with a Church that is founded on divorce, even though I feel a hypocrite saying it, being a divorcee like you."

"Don't be. The Church of England has at least acknowledged that we can all make mistakes, some more serious than others."

They carried on eating their supper. It occurred to Marjorie that Arthur was probably trying to make sense of his first marriage and why it had gone so wrong. At least her short lived marriage had not produced any children.

"Do you believe in an afterlife?" She asked.

"If you are referring to life after our existence, I think our existence was probably before we had a life. I often think we are here on earth for a purpose, to find love, to give love and finally give up love, leaving those behind us, to do the same thing, live by our example. It sounds depressing, but it shouldn't be. I think life is beautiful, if not challenging. It sets various obstacles along our path and we have to negotiate them. Provided we negotiate the right path, we will have a fulfilled life. Don't get me wrong, chance plays a significant factor. I'm a scientist. I will often purport to have the answers to everything, but rarely is the whole of creation solvable."

Arthur stood up and went to the bar to get some more drinks in. Marjorie carried on eating the shepherds pie. When he returned, placing the glasses on the table, she asked.

"It must have been difficult to qualify as a scientist at Cambridge and then re-evaluate your religious beliefs with the science, that is, if you are religious?"

"Oh I believe in a greater being, I just haven't met him yet."

"You said at our last lunch that when your time is up, it's up. I don't think you can do much to control destiny." She argued.

"More's the pity! I was hoping that after the Planetarium, we had a little bit more control of ours. But there's my point, you have galaxy after galaxy of constellations, millions of light years away. It's mind boggling. I don't think we can ever comprehend the universe or try to. I have huge respect for it, who doesn't? But, the long and short of it is when we die we die. I think the most important mission for human beings is love and the ability to bring new love in to the world."

Marjorie paused for thought. How had she missed so much in the earlier years of her life? She had been so locked in to herself just letting life pass her by. She had if she was honest with herself spent too much time on her own, brooding about her lot in life.

After that evening in the Flask, she continued to see Arthur most evenings after work. They just seemed to get into an inevitable routine. Sometimes, they would just meet for a drink as he often had to work late in the City. Arthur had a high profile job as chemical engineer with BP. She did not pertain to understand what he did as it was extremely technical, mostly graphical analyses of the chemical degradation of oil at different temperatures in different climates. All she knew was that he had to work long hours and that it was extremely stressful. She liked to think that seeing her, helped to relax him. He would always have to cut short these evenings during the week to get back to his house in North London.

At the weekends, Marjorie would go and see him at his house in Barnet. It was a lovely semi detached house with a beautiful garden. The best bit was the willow tree in the garden where they would hang out in the spring when the first shoots were coming up in the garden such as daffodils and snowdrops. She often helped in the garden, pruning back the roses and digging up the weeds. The garden felt part of them in some way, continually evolving and growing into beautiful flowers.

One sunny day they were sitting on the bench outside the kitchen, nursing a small sherry and some biscuits.

"I don't know what it is about gardening and getting older. They seem to go hand in hand."

"You're not that old," he replied, patting her on the back gently. By now Arthur knew most things about Marjorie, including her age. They had no need for secrets.

"I love the feeling when spring has sprung, when all the first shoots start coming through."

"Like a garden bursting in to life." He offered.

"Something like that."

"I'd better start preparing something to eat."

With that Marjorie stood up and smoothed down her apron. She loved cooking for Arthur, even if it was just a simple three egg omelette. She loved caring for him as well as making his house a home. Luckily for her this house had no traces of his previous marriage, as he had given up the marital home to his ex wife. She had never had these feelings for somebody before. They were all consuming, like the garden that needed their constant attention.

He in turn, gave her the confidence she had been desperately lacking. Even though she was in her forties, she still hadn't passed her driving test. Many had tried to teach her, each one flattening her resolve.

Arthur would often pick her up from the train station in North London where his house was and allow them to swap seats so that she could take control of the car.

"It's very simple, you just press down on the clutch and then select the gears, slowly ease off the clutch and put pressure on the accelerator."

He would place his hands over Marjorie's and gently offer the instruction. His touch was strong and firm. To Marjorie, he felt very in control, but it was her feet doing the work.

"Think of it like playing the piano, easing your feet off the pedals to the variance in the vibrato."

He would never scold her or raise a hand. If she made a mistake, he would just chortle with laughter and tell her to start again.

"Oh please don't laugh." She said laughing with him.

"I can't help it if you drive like a jumping kangaroo." He responded.

"I'll get the better of you." And with that he would often bend down and give her a loving peck on the forehead.

"I love you when you are flustered."

Eventually after nine months, Marjorie met his teenage sons. They took them out at the weekend, either to the beach or the park. They both came to realize that what they had was serious. Their love for each other was very strong. She could not bear to be without him.

They would often take them to see her mother in Margate, so that his two sons could play on the arcades. The smell of sweet candy floss used to permeate the air, interacting with the sour smell of vinegar, fish and chips. The resort oozed fun on the sands. The donkeys would slowly plod up and down the beach, whilst the children were screaming in and out of the waves of the ocean. Marjorie could see Arthur loved those excursions with his sons. He would roll up his slacks, take off his shoes and socks and run in and out of the sea with them, leaping over the piles of seaweed. Her heart ached to one day have children with this man, to give him the opportunity to have a proper family again. However there was no hiding the fact that her biological clock was ticking.

MIRIAM 1965
DUBLIN

WHEN MIRIAM GOT home that evening after that wonderful night with Len, she arrived to find Orla slumped with her head down on the kitchen table. She had obviously been crying as there were mounds of tissues everywhere. There was an empty glass of what looked like the remnants of a whisky on the table.

"What's up sis?" She asked.

"You won't fecking believe it! Patrick's only got me fecking pregnant."

"Jesus holy Mother of God, what will mum say! She won't let us be pregnant unless we're married. She will see it as bringing shame on the family."

"I know, I know, but she doesn't believe in abortion either. She thinks that is the ultimate Catholic sin as well."

"Does Patrick know?"

"Of course he fecking knows. It bloody ruined our evening. He's gone out to get pissed and won't be back until morning, that irresponsible little shit."

"You need to talk about this together sis. You can't do this on your own."

"For the Mother of God don't you think I know that? Don't what ever you do get in to this mess. I don't care how much they say they love you, men are just after one thing. Now I am well and truly stuffed."

The feelings Miriam had for Len that evening were still raw in her chest. She knew she was in love with this man. Surely if you loved someone, it would all come right in the end? Surely if Patrick and her sister talked, he would do the right thing by her. Although the sexual revolution of the 1960s was in full swing in England, not Ireland, family planners, insisted you wore a wedding ring to receive contraception and took a dim view of sex outside marriage. There was no question of an abortion. In those days it was illegal unless you went to a back-street abortionist in England or paid an expensive consultant in London. Their parents and most of the doctors around were of a generation that lived within the rules. Miriam's generation were a generation that wanted to change the rules.

"You need to talk to Patrick. See if he will make an honest woman of you. If you act now it might not be too late."

"Don't you think I frigging know that sis? I'm up the duff and he's on the piss."

"Calm down, calm down. He's probably in shock right now like you are. Give him time, he will come round."

"I haven't got time sis. If he won't marry me then I'm going to have to resort to some drastic measures. We just don't have the money."

Miriam's heart went out to her sister that night. She had some money, but not a lot. They were so close as a family, it would break their hearts if their mother disowned them. She only wanted what was best for her girls. She was also staunchly Catholic. She would not accept any child out of wedlock. Miriam grabbed herself a tumbler and poured herself a whisky. She asked her sister if she wanted another one, but she refused, thinking at the very least she would try and give her mite a little chance.

"Maybe we should go and see Father Amon and seek his advice?

"What! And risk the whole community knowing. I can't risk it sis."

That night Miriam put her sister to bed and drank another whisky and smoked a cigarette. She had such a wonderful evening it seemed cruel that it should end with this demise. She didn't know Len well enough to confide in him. He would probably help if she asked, but she could risk losing him. The most important thing to sort out now was Patrick. They would have to talk to him tomorrow if he was going to be in any fit state to talk to that is.

Miriam slept fretfully that night tossing and turning. Her thoughts were with Len and the lovely evening they had had and then switched to her sister and the mess she had got herself into. It rained heavily that night, the rain pounding against the windows, dripping on to the roofs below. It was as if the heavens were opening that night, pouring out their grief for the situation they found themselves in. Miriam curled up in a ball and pulled the covers tightly around her. Her parents would never accept her sister's demise unless she was married. Even then they were bound to suspect something. They hadn't even met Patrick yet, let alone accepted him. As the night wore on the rain gradually turned to a patter. The darkness began to fade to light. Miriam didn't know what time it was, but she heard a door slam in the early hours and some footsteps climb the stairs to Orla's room. Finally she dozed off waiting for the dawn to begin.

Her sister and Patrick were sat at the kitchen table when she surfaced the following morning. Patrick looked a little worse for wear, his hair slightly dishevelled. Her sister's eyes were red from crying. She looked exhausted. She clearly had not had a wink of sleep. She lit the gas stove and put the kettle on. There was a dull silence in the air.

"Anyone for a cup of tea?" Miriam asked

"I guess Orla has told you," said Patrick, looking up at her.

"Yes." Miriam replied.

She knew her sister would have chastised him for staying out late last night. The fact that he had come home at all was a starting point. Her sister got up to get some orange juice from the fridge. Patrick dragged his hands through his hair and then reached for a packet of cigarettes on the table.

"The thing is do you want this baby?"

"No, I want to frigging kill it you idiot! What do you think I want to do?" her sister retorted.

"Well, it's just that we've never discussed children before."

"Do you think I planned this?"

"Calm down sis, we have to deal with the present."

They discussed the fact that neither of their families would cope with children out of wedlock. Patrick's family were fiercely Catholic too. Whilst Patrick hadn't planned to get married, he wanted to do the right thing by her sister. He said he didn't have the best job in the world, but maybe they could move to London and he would get more lucrative freelance work there. He was a builder by trade and lots of his mates had done just that.

"Maybe we could have a small Registry Office wedding in Dublin and then get a ferry to England. Maybe Miriam can be one of our witnesses?"

"What will mum say?"

"You'll have to tell her sis."

"But she will go through the roof!"

"Surely she won't if you tell her you're getting married. If you keep it a quiet affair then the family won't be embarrassed. We could go and see them today."

Miriam's sister then burst into tears. She couldn't bear the thought of their parent's reaction. How would they cope with the shame of it all? They had always talked of a big wedding ceremony for the both of them when the time came, lots of guests and a big family reception. Her sister was now going to deny them the pride of such an occasion. A shot gun wedding with an elopement to England.

The telephone rang. Nobody wanted to pick it up for fear it was their parents. Miriam went to pick it up.

"Hi it's me, Len."

"Hi."

"Do you feel like doing something today?"

"Oh Len I'd love to, but we have a bit of a family crisis I'm afraid. Maybe some other time."

"Fine, your call, see you soon."

And with that he put the phone down. Miriam felt terrible, as if she had stabbed him in the back. Would he ever call her again? She wanted more than anything to go out with him that day but her sister was in a terrible state. She couldn't just leave her.

"Who was that?"

"Oh nothing. It can wait. We need to go and see mum. Patrick, do you agree?"

"Yes."

With that they all went to their bedrooms to get changed. Having put on their smart attire, Patrick offered to drive them to their parent's house just outside Cork. The journey would take about three hours. Orla took a grocery bag as a sick bag, just in case she was sick on the way. The drive was quite subdued as they took the road out of Dublin and then through the undulating green countryside. Miriam's thoughts were of Len and when she would next see him. She wondered how he would have reacted to this situation? After all, he had been married before and had two children. Would he stand by her as Patrick was doing for her sister?"

The roads were still wet from the heavy rain the night before. The sun was trying to break through the clouds. They tuned in the radio to the sound of the Moody Blues and "Nights in White Satin". Every now and then Patrick would put a reassuring hand on Orla's knee. She was queasy, but didn't feel sick. No one spoke throughout that journey. They were all worried about their parent's impending reaction. What if they decided to shun her sister altogether for her actions and decide to never speak to her again? Surely they wouldn't, not if her sister was getting married?

After two and a half hours of driving, which seemed like an eternity, they pulled in to their parent's drive and leapt out of the car. There were their two springer spaniels there, that had grown up with them, to greet them. Miriam was the first to enter the kitchen. The Aga was ticking over to the gurgling noise of the oil.

"What a nice surprise Miriam! You didn't tell us you were coming."

In truth she hadn't thought about ringing ahead beforehand. She had just sort of assumed in the commotion of it all that they would always be there. They never strayed far from the home, only venturing out to see close friends and family every now and then at their local.

"I've brought my sis and her boyfriend too. Patrick meet my parents."

They exchanged handshakes and pleasantries and slowly made their way to the kitchen table. Miriam's mother was eyeing Orla strangely. They didn't normally turn up unannounced like this. Their parents usually liked to have some warning of their pending arrival, so their mother could make a fuss over them. The small grandfather clock ticked in the background. Her mum started to put on the kettle.

"So what's brought on this lovely surprise then?"

Miriam's sister sat awkwardly on the chair, her fingers twisting in her lap. She tried to speak, but the words wouldn't come out of her. Miriam could see the stress of the last few days weighing down on her. Her eyes were heavy from crying. She couldn't gauge whether her mother noticed anything strange.

"The thing is Mrs Sullivan-Cody we have something to tell you. Your daughter and I are going to get married." Patrick blurted out.

"Shouldn't you be asking my permission young man?" Her father interjected.

"You're bloody pregnant, that's what this is about."

Their mother was never prone to swearing, but clearly the anger had got the better of her now. Miriam's sister had now brought shame on their family and their mother was not going to tolerate this without a fight.

"Mum, listen it's not like that."

"Why else would you announce that you are getting married to someone I've never seen before." Their mum yelled.

"I don't want to cause you any further embarrassment than I already have. Yes, I am pregnant, but we plan to get married straight away in a Registry Office in Dublin. We're then going to London where we plan to have the baby."

Everyone could see the tears of frustration building up in her mother's eyes. She slumped down on the wooden chair beside her and took out a tissue to wipe her nose. Her father leant down and put a comforting arm around her.

"I always thought I'd taught you to be good Catholic girls, to adhere to the strict rules of Catholicism for your own protection, not just the family's reputation. No amount of Hail Mary's or confessions in the confessional box will give you God's forgiveness for what you have done. Our ancestors fought tirelessly for the right to remain Catholic in Ireland. What part didn't you listen to? What is happening to your generation?"

Her sister got up from her chair and knelt down on her knees. Her eyes tried to engage her mother's, but her face was now buried in her hands on the table.

"That is why we are trying to do the right thing by this child and get married well before it is due. We don't mean to cause you or our families any further embarrassment."

Miriam could see her parents were disappointed, disappointed that their daughter had got herself into this mess, disappointed that they could not have a proper family wedding. Her father was not as staunchly Catholic as her mother, but he was a man of principle. After a long and agonizing silence he reluctantly stepped forward to offer to shake Patrick's hand. Miriam could see a lot of remorse etched on his face that day.

"At least you are doing the decent thing by her my son. Make sure you take good care of her."

Miriam's mother got up and said nothing more of it. She had made her feelings known and that was the end of it as far as she was concerned. No doubt she would come around over time, but for now her utter disapproval was clear to all. She stood up and walked to the kitchen sink staring out of the window to the countryside beyond.

The rest of them sat down round the kitchen table and started to talk about plans for the wedding. Their father decided that he and their mother would not be present. It was best to get the wedding out of the way as soon as possible, to avoid any further embarrassment. An announcement would be made in the local paper. There was no time for a church wedding. In any event it seemed entirely inappropriate for her sister to have a church wedding as she had gone against God's wishes by getting pregnant out of wedlock. They had a stilted cup of tea and some biscuits. A celebration did not seem appropriate at this time even though Patrick was doing the right thing by Miriam's sister. They finally said their goodbyes and headed back to Dublin that evening.

"You'd better not make the same mistake I've made sis, it would kill mum and dad."

"I won't." Miriam replied. All she knew in her head that if she got married it would have to be for love, true unconditional love. Her head was spinning with thoughts of Len. When would she next see him? Had she blown it this morning when he called her and she'd put him off? She couldn't bear not to see him again.

The following Monday, Miriam took the day off to help organize the wedding at the Registry Office in Dublin. The woman at the office said that it was most irregular to organize a wedding at such short notice, but there was a cancellation the following Saturday. They would need at least two witnesses and a copy of her sister and Patrick's birth certificates. If they failed to make it on time they would have to go back on the waiting list.

Miriam and her sister went for lunch that day to buy a wedding dress. They didn't want to go to the store Miriam worked in. It would send too many alarm bells ringing, so they settled for a little store down a side street that did designer clothes suitable to go to a wedding. Her sister didn't want to draw too much attention to herself, even though the wedding was to take place in Dublin with no family present. She chose a light cream Chanel styled suit and a pale chiffon scarf. The suit fitted perfectly, and there were no signs at present that she was pregnant. Miriam chose an egg shell dress with matching shoes and a fake pearl necklace.

"We'll get some flowers on the day, sis and some button holes for the men."

"Who are you bringing Miriam?"

"Oh I haven't decided yet, it has all happened so fast."

"You could ask Len to come along."

"Oh I don't know. He might draw the wrong conclusions."

In truth she had thought about asking him, but having turned him down when he last phoned, she didn't know whether he would bother to contact her again. Her emotions had been so enveloped with her sister's predicament, she hadn't dared phone him back that weekend. He probably thought she was avoiding him. She also didn't want to create a bad impression. Getting pregnant out of wedlock was a foolish predicament to get yourself into and she didn't want Len to think she would do something similar. Not that they had reached that stage in their relationship yet. That was an entirely different hurdle to overcome.

The rest of the week Miriam carried on working at Brown Thomas. Customers came and went. Mrs O Grady seemed pleased with her progress, the way she dealt with each customer, tending to their every requirement. Some returned to pick up their tailored suits, others came in for alterations. She picked out the perfect ties and shirts to match and made sure the client was happy with their purchases.

"I think you're getting the hang of this young lady. We should think about moving you to another department. Think of it as a promotion."

That Friday, just as Miriam was finishing rolling the fabrics, Len strode in and came straight up to the counter.

"I want to return this tie."

"What's wrong with it ?" She asked.

"It's a bit lewd don't you think," he smiled. "For a wedding."

"How did you know?"

"Pat told me, said that's why you haven't returned any of my calls. Well come on then, are you going to change it?"

"Miriam I suggest you serve this gentleman." Mrs O'Grady barked.

Miriam took Len by his arm and led him to the tie section.

"You could have got me in trouble." She whispered.

"Are you going to invite me to the wedding then?"

"It's going to be a very quiet affair, but now that my boss knows about it!" She hissed.

"I missed you."

With that he brushed her cheek with his hand and held her eyes. She missed him too, she wanted to tell him, with every bone of her body. She could have kissed him then, but her mind quickly turned to the fact that Mrs O'Grady's eyes were firmly on her. She knew she had to sort out his tie and then get him to leave as soon as possible before she suspected anything.

"Meet me at O'Neills after work and we'll discuss it then," she murmured, catching her boss's eye. "Perhaps this tie would suit you sir?" she said slightly louder than she should have done. She chose him a pale blue tie to match her dress and then he left.

When Miriam got to the pub that evening, the place was heaving. Friday nights were always packed. Orla and Patrick were sat with the usual crowd Pat and Humphrey. Len was sat next to Pat, engaging her in conversation. He looked at ease in the company of her friends. As she approached, he turned and stood up to fetch her a stool.

"You didn't get demoted then?" He asked

"I was about to be promoted before you came in!" She laughed.

He led her gently to the bar and they ordered their drinks with ease. The noise in the bar was becoming increasingly deafening as the punters were piling in from work.

"So, am I invited tomorrow then, to your sister's wedding?"

"Well I haven't got anyone else to take if that is what you are implying."

"I will pick you up at eleven then."

The following day they all met up outside the Registry Office in Sheep Street. Miriam collected the roses to put in their buttonholes from the florist first thing that morning. Len looked extremely handsome in a dark navy suit with the pale blue tie, she had chosen for him. There was an air of excitement surrounding their small group which consisted of Pat and Humphrey as witnesses for Patrick and Miriam and Len as witnesses for her sister. There were a number of couples before them and so they had to wait their turn in the waiting room.

"Are you nervous sis?"

"Just a little." She replied.

"Don't worry, it will be over before you know it."

"That is what I am afraid of."

Len was stood up, pacing the room. It felt as if they were in some doctor's waiting room. The walls were pretty bare and slightly tired-looking. The round clock on the wall above the door, ticked away, breaking the silence. Finally a woman in black uniform called their names and they were ushered into a small office with a large mahogany desk and a suited man with rounded spectacles seated behind it. As the words stared to tumble from his mouth.

"We are gathered here today to witness the marriage of Patrick to Orla."

Miriam turned and glanced at Len. His eyes were slightly sad, she thought, as if he was regretting the vows he had taken. She couldn't tell from his expression, what he was thinking. She knew nothing, she realized about his first wife or what she looked like. Suddenly thoughts of her intrigued her. If only she could see a photo of her?

"Do you take this woman to be your lawful wedded wife? To have and to hold from this day forward, for richer and poorer, in sickness and health, until death do us part?"

"I do."

Patrick and Orla then exchanged their rings and gave each other a tender kiss. How Miriam longed for this commitment from someone one day, to entirely belong to one another. She had not been seeing Len long enough to know if he was the one, but she knew that she was in danger of falling seriously in love with this man. In some ways, she was jealous of his first wife, jealous of the fact that he married her and had his children. She knew nothing about them, or how much he still loved them. He must have loved them one day and that hurt.

"I now pronounce you man and wife."

Orla flung her arms around Patrick's neck and gave him a kiss. Len and Humphrey patted Patrick on the back and they all exchanged embraces. Miriam wished her mum and dad had been there to see her sister getting married. They would have been so proud of her. They had decided to stay away to draw less attention to the whole event, yet still, she was their daughter. Len put his protective arm around her and they stepped out of the Registry Office. Humphrey and Pat took some photos and then they headed to a restaurant that they had booked at the Brooks Hotel where Orla and Patrick were going to spend their honeymoon night.

They ordered champagne and toasted the bride and groom. They ordered a set menu of oysters, salmon and then noisettes of lamb with colcannon.

"Was this like your wedding?" Miriam asked. She didn't want to talk about his wedding, but the wine was doing the talking.

"Oh I'm afraid ours was rather a grand affair. I think we invited over one hundred and fifty people. The reception was at my ex wife's house, just outside Cork."

"What was she like, your ex wife I mean?"

He hesitated whilst he thought about this one. He didn't want to offend her.

"She was beautiful to look at, but not in person. She married more out of obligation than anything else."

How beautiful was she Miriam thought? Was she more beautiful than her? She desperately wanted the answers but daren't ask for fear of losing him. How long had he married her for, she thought, and how long would she need to see him before the memories of her were obliterated? Maybe they would never be, because his children would always be there as a constant reminder of what could have been.

"We should explore Dublin, you and me, pretend we are tourists. I want to spend every waking moment with you."

Humphrey proposed a toast and lunch rolled into the evening. Everyone, by this stage, was very merry and bursting into song.

Miriam loved those Irish evenings when everybody got together and had a sing song. It reminded her of times they had spent together at their parent's house. Any excuse for a party. She had never felt that home feeling in London. Len and Miriam had agreed to meet up the following day outside Trinity College.

"See you tomorrow." She said when they kissed goodnight.

"Yes, see you then."

Over the following months, they explored the softer side of Dublin, drinking in the city's culture and history. The architecture was a bit of a jumble, but the soul and sociability of the place made up for the fact that Dublin was no oil painting. They ambled through the landscaped parks and engaged with Dublin's myriad cultural offerings. Miriam remembered hearing on the radio at that time "It is often said that Dublin on the River Liffey is the political and population hub of Ireland, busy quickening to today's tempo, but not forgetting its' great men of the past, Swift and Burton, Sheridan and Joyce and many many others who have lent glory to the nation."

"You have a vision for fashion, and I have a vision for architecture." He said.

Georgian architecture in Dublin had come under attack by the Irish Government's development policies. Whole swathes of eighteenth century houses were being demolished notably in Fitzwilliam Street and St Stephen's Green to make way for utilitarian office blocks and government departments.

"I want to design modern architecture that inspires. Simple clean lines, encompassing modern living. There is a lot of money in it at the moment, because the property market is so buoyant. We've got investors screaming all over the place to get involved."

"Aren't you taking a risk?" Miriam said "If the property market crashes?"

"No, because the key is to demolish the building, get a grant as fast as we can and then turn the development round and move on. The trick is, not to sit on any development too long. There is a nationalist ideology at the moment, that wants to wipe away all physical reminders of our Irish colonial past. I don't necessarily agree with this ideology, but it is a great way to make money."

"Oh Len, I can't believe you sometimes, all you think about is making money!" she said nudging his ribs.

"Well, I've got some expensive mouths to feed."

Miriam didn't know in that split second whether he was referring to her, his ex, his children or both.

Sometimes they would mingle with the shoppers on Cumberland's second hand market, or watch the Corpus Christi processions through the City of Dublin. But most of the time they would drink in his vision of Dublin. They would roam the streets of Kildare, Harcourt and North Great George Street, going through his next projects. She enjoyed watching him at work. He would often show her the plans and introduce her to some of his colleagues at work. She liked the fact that he felt, she was someone that he could introduce to his colleagues, that he valued her opinion. Most of them were a lot older than her, and many had travelled with Len to South Africa. One of her favorites was Donald, who was slightly bald and overweight, but still a lot of fun. Donald came from a long line of Irish descendants.

"I'm the professional artist in the family! Piss-artist that is. I'll never forget the time with Len in South Africa, when we were on safari. We were flying a small light aircraft in to the Kalahari desert when we had engine failure. We only had to land the plane in a herd of buffalos. I don't know who was more scared, the buffalos or us!"

Miriam imagined this far away existence that Len had, had with his colleagues. Apparently they had been involved in some huge project out there, which was nearly at a close. Donald was still overseeing the project over there, whilst Len concentrated on Dublin.

One night they were sitting and having a drink in O'Neills, when they heard a large bomb go off. The walls shook and the ground beneath them rumbled. About twenty minutes later, a guy ran in to the pub shouting.

"Someone has only fecking bombed Nelson's Pillar in O'Connell Street. Reckon it is the Republican Army."

These were troubled times in Northern and Southern Ireland. The IRA as they were known, were becoming more of a force to be reckoned with, particularly in Macroom. This statue was a famous british admiral, and had been a landmark for a Century.

"They've done that just before the fifty year commemorations of the Easter Rising." said Donald.

If they weren't frequenting the Irish pubs of the Temple district, they would be out in a convoy of cars to the races. Len always had a gamble on the horses and mostly won. They discussed buying a race horse and tried to think of some witty names to call it. Miriam enjoyed being in their company as well as having the times with Len to herself.

She rarely spoke to her sister. She was so absorbed with her new life in Dublin. The occasional times she did speak to her, she would say that Patrick and her were arguing a lot and that as the pregnancy was progressing she was feeling more and more uncomfortable.

"We've got a new flat just off Muswell Hill. You'll have to come and visit sis."

"I will. I just don't have time at the moment."

"How's it going with Len?"

"Oh fine! We're having so much fun. He is taking me to Kinsale next weekend, to a small hotel in the harbour."

"I'm not being funny sis, but is this guy ready to commit? I know with Patrick, men are only after one thing. Don't go there sis."

"I'm fine"

That weekend, Len picked Miriam up in his E Type Jaguar, outside Brown Thomas, much to the approving glances of Mrs O'Grady and whisked her down the country lanes to Kinsale. Once they had left the dreary grey buildings of Dublin, they drove through the luscious green countryside with little white-washed houses either side of the road, listening to Dionne Warwick on the radio. They arrived in Kinsale, just as it was getting dark. As they stepped out of the car, it was lovely to hear the waves splashing against the rocks with the seagulls circling overhead. You could smell the fish in the ocean.

"I've booked us into a sweet hotel around the corner. I thought we could check-in and then check-out the hotel restaurant."

Len took their cases to the hotel reception and checked them in to two double rooms next to each other. When they got upstairs they went to Miriam's room and poured themselves two whiskies. He lit her cigarette and they chatted for awhile.

"How's your sister doing in London?"

"Oh she's fine. Her baby is due soon. I'll be an Aunty!"

She couldn't gauge his expression. Perhaps he was worried in case she might become broody. Whatever it was it soon faded.

"I don't know about you, but I fancy a trip to London. I may have a development opportunity coming up soon."

Miriam snuggled into him.

"That doesn't mean you're going to leave me in Dublin does it?"

"No, I'll be back and forth."

When they'd finished their whiskies, they went downstairs to the restaurant. They were the only diners there, forcing them to speak in whispers, whilst the waiters were eavesdropping.

"I don't think they can understand a word that we are saying, they are all French, I think!" Len laughed.

They shared their Parisian moment with a bottle, or was it two of Chablis? They then walked round the quay and stared out to sea at the moon reflecting on the water. They then popped in to a local pub, where a local band was playing some Irish folk music. The place was full of Irish singers dancing and laughing, clapping and stamping their feet to the rhythm. They joined in with the rest of them, polishing off a few night caps before retiring to their bedroom, with not a care in the world.

For many weeks after that, when they returned to Dublin, Miriam would stay at his flat, just off Parnell Square. Despite his love of modern architecture, his flat was in a beautiful Georgian building, filled with glorious antiques. Her sister gave birth to a baby girl, Charlotte. Their lives were falling blissfully into place.

MARJORIE 1966
LONDON

B Y NOW THEIR relationship had fallen in to a routine and Marjorie would spend most of her time with Arthur. Her biological clock was ticking. She was now forty-three years of age and soon she wouldn't be able to have children. Arthur and she, had started to talk about marriage and what effect it would have on Arthur's sons. Marjorie thought they liked her, but she had never plucked up the courage to ask Arthur about it. She had always worried about rejection in her life, ever since boarding school. The fear of being too fat. The fear that the girls in her class, didn't like her enough. But for now, time was not on her side.

"Have you asked the boys whether they would approve of us getting married?"

Marjorie plucked up the courage and asked, as they were sat in a pub off Hadley Green, nursing two halves of cider.

"No." He replied. "But I know they like you and that they are not that fond of their mother."

"She must have hurt them badly, if they don't love her."

"Oh she was a bad mother and a bad wife. I never thought I would find love again as I've found with you. That's why I want us to get married. I know you don't speak of it, but you must want children."

"There is nothing I would rather have in all the world with you and I'm not getting any younger." She replied with a knowing smile.

"I'm glad I waited all this time for you to come along, as had I married sooner I would never have known what it was like to meet a true soulmate."

At that point, a tiny sparrow, landed on the wooden table, pecked on a few discarded crumbs and then darted off again. The birds were singing in the background. You could hear the faint rumbling of the traffic in the distance.

"You know, if we do get married, we probably won't be able to get married in a church. They don't tend to approve of divorcees, you know."

With that he slowly circled the edge of his glass with his forefinger.

"We can always get married in a Registry Office." Marjorie replied. "It doesn't mean God doesn't approve."

They continued to sit opposite each other taking small gulps from the refreshing cider. In the background they could hear the faint hum of a lawnmower, from someone cutting the grass. It left a delicious smell of greenery in the air. The pub was starting to fill up with people, popping in for a quick pint after work. The wooden benches stretched out on to the common, packed with city workers just back from their commute. The laughter crescendoed as the pints kept rolling in.

"Lets go back to Dalmeny Road. I've got something to show you."

With that he picked up his brief case and overcoat and they made their way to the car. She didn't offer to drive on this occasion. She liked it when he took control. The car smelt of old leather, newly polished the previous weekend. The walnut dashboard glowed in the evening sunlight. She turned her head towards Arthur to see the light reflecting on his slightly ruffled hair.

When they got back to his house, Arthur told Marjorie to go in to the garden, whilst he fetched two sherry glasses. The evening song birds were now in full flourish. A slow faint breeze, rustled through the willow trees. She could hear Arthur place the glasses down on the sideboard and walk to the living room to turn on the radio. A few minutes later, she heard the sound of Mozart emanate through the kitchen windows.

"Here, take this," he said handing her a glass. He then placed his hands in his trouser pockets and brought out an exquisite little leather square box lightly embossed with gold.

"I'm not very good at getting down on one bended knee, I'm afraid, but I think you know what is coming."

She smiled. In all the time she had known Arthur he was not very good at keeping a secret. She had anticipated he would ask sooner rather than later. She jumped up and flung her arms around his warm neck. She could feel the hairs on his neck, standing up on end, beneath his aromatic aftershave.

"Of course I will," she said, with tears in her eyes. He handed her the box, inside of which was a beautiful diamond and ruby ring, the one she had seen at the jewellers, the previous weekend but had not said anything, fearing it was too expensive. She gingerly handed him the ring to put on her wedding finger. She then turned her hand to allow the evening sun to cast a reflection on the stones.

"It's beautiful."

"So are you."

That night they watched the sun go down with only each other for company. They discussed who they would invite to the wedding and where the wedding should take place. They also made sure they put in a telephone call to his boys who were both over the moon for them. They didn't want the wedding to be a grand affair, just a few close family and friends. As this was the second time for both of them they didn't want a fuss.

"I don't want to rush things, but I'd love to get married sooner rather than later."

"Me too."

Her life was now complete. All they had to do was finalize the arrangements. Over the next few weeks they approached a number of vicars. They wanted God's blessing, but they all politely declined. They were of the opinion that they should settle for a Registry Office. Finally a friend of hers, Joy suggested she try the chapel at Westminster Abbey.

"He is a very nice vicar and I have heard that he does sanctify second marriages."

"I'm not being funny, but doesn't it sound a bit grand, Westminster Abbey I mean. We both agreed we wanted a low key affair."

"It won't be in the main Abbey, it will just be in the small chapel to the right. If you have a word with him and meet him I'm sure you'll be a lot happier."

The service was arranged and only close family were invited. Apart from having to negotiate the crowds of tourists trying to visit the Abbey, the service went without a hitch and they were duly blessed by the vicar and made their vows.

"To have and to hold from this day forward, until death us do part."

When the ceremony was finished they gathered outside in the sunshine to have their photographs taken. The bells chimed against the thunderous commuter traffic outside the gardens of Westminster. She saw a lifetime together of sharing everything that day. Her life suddenly felt so complete. By having God's blessing, she felt nothing could harm them or take them away from each other.

After the honeymoon in the Channel Islands, spent with lots of lazy days on the beaches, they pretty much settled into married life in Dalmeny Road. Marjorie was the epitome housewife, cleaning the house, ironing Arthur's shirts for his next day at work and cooking supper for when he returned home. Arthur would be exhausted after his long hours at work in the City, but they would always make time for each other. She would never pry him about work, because in any event most of what he did was above her head. She made sure that once Arthur was home nothing else should pray on his mind. At the weekends, they would take a long walk in the woods and sometimes visit the local pub. These were happy times. There was no threat of war or anything else to take this away from them.

The only thing missing in their lives was a child.

MIRIAM 1967
DUBLIN

AS THE MONTHS went by, Miriam felt sure of her feelings for Len. He was a charmer and she knew that he was attractive to most women, but there again she was attractive to most men. She knew his colleagues fancied her even though they dare not make a pass at her. They knew that she belonged to Len. He would always put a protective arm around her. He would never let go of her eyes in his company. He would send her little notes of affection when she was not with him. She had fallen for him, but had no idea, if he had fallen for her.

It was a cold winters day in February 1967, in the lead up to Valentines Day, when Miriam realized she had missed her period by three weeks. That morning she called in sick to work and made an appointment to see a doctor in Harcourt Street, Dr Riley. She counted the numbers along the street. It was a road that seemed to go on forever. She found the right one, number twenty four. It was a rather grand georgian building. It looked more like an office than a clinic. She paused by the front door, catching her breath. She held her bag with both hands in front of her and nudged the door open. The waiting room was to the left of the entrance hall and had about ten people waiting. There was rather an ornate fireplace with a small gas fire. On the coffee table were piles of magazines with stick-thin models such as Twiggy, showing the latest sixties fashion. How Miriam longed to be on one of those covers right now. Slowly people came in and out of the doctor's surgery. The receptionist, directed each person to their appointments, when it was their turn. Surely, she couldn't be pregnant, they had been so careful?

"Miriam Sullivan-Cody?"

She stood up and looked around her. She didn't look pregnant or feel pregnant even. She gingerly opened the door and went to sit down in front of Dr Riley. She was a woman in her forties with slicked-back blond hair and glasses. Her hand shake was brisk.

"So, how can I help you then?"

"I think I may be pregnant."

"Are you married?"

"No."

A silence hung in the air. She looked Miriam straight in the eyes and with clinical composure took out a small plastic package.

"Well then, we will need to keep this discreet. You will need to do a urine sample in the toilet outside and then come back, so that we can take the test."

She handed Miriam a small test tube and with that, she exited the room to go to the toilet. Is this how her sister felt all those months ago when she found out she was pregnant with Charlotte? Did she have that horrible pit feeling in her stomach? She made her way to the ladies' toilet, past the line of eyes watching her. Once in the toilet, she pulled on the light and looked in the mirror. She put her bag down on the floor and did the urine sample. She then made her way back to the waiting room, past the other patients waiting, to see the doctor.

The doctor opened a drawer from her desk and took out a small testing kit. She took her urine sample, which Miriam had handed to her and with a pipette put two drops of clear liquid in to her test tube sample.

"This shouldn't take long."

She watched as the test tube gradually changed colour from a golden yellow to a deep blue hue. Miriam's entire future lay with that test tube. She saw the doctor scrutinize the colour with a chart. For a few moments, she wondered, what the doctor was looking at. It simply could not take that long to look at a sample.

"I'm afraid it's bad news, or good news, however you want to take it, you are pregnant."

The tears welled up in Miriam's eyes, waiting to fall. She reached for a tissue out of her bag and dabbed her eyes.

"If you are considering the possibility of terminating this pregnancy, then I strongly suggest that you go by recommendation."

With that the doctor filled out a form for Miriam to sign and then she picked up her bag and walked back through reception. The surgery was now full of people. No one was talking to anyone else, anxious not to acknowledge that there was anyone in the room.

Miriam left the surgery in a whirlwind of emotions. How would Len take it? How could she now pursue a career in fashion design? This was not part of the plan. Her parents would go berserk. They couldn't handle this twice. The indignity of it all. She wandered the streets aimlessly. Suddenly the buildings held no comfort for her any more. She longed to be by the sea, to feel the ebb and tide of the ocean. Is this what God had destined for her? Inside her was another life, a symbol of the love she had for Len. She couldn't tell Len just yet. She needed to collect her thoughts.

She made her way to the Arbour Hill Cemetery, just north of Odlins barracks. This small cemetery was the final resting place of all the fourteen executed Leaders of the 1916 Easter Rising. The burial ground was plain with the fourteen names inscribed in stone. Beside the graves, was a cenotaph, bearing the Easter Proclammation. She could not imagine ending this life she had just begun. She sat on a stone wall, tears streaming down her face. She felt angry with herself for getting herself in to this situation, particularly after her sister's predicament. What would she say?

When she got back to her apartment, Len called.

"Do you fancy meeting up later?"

She steadied herself against the console in the hallway and looked at her reflection in the mirror in front of her. Her eyes were heavy and red. There was no way she could meet up with Len in this state.

"You know what, can we leave it until Valentine's day? I'm not feeling so good."

She knew Len would find this strange. She never normally passed him up on a drink. A small silence ensued.

"You're not pregnant are you? Heaven forbid." He said laughing hesitantly.

"No."

"Well I guess I'll just have to wait until Valentine's day then. I've booked Wheelers. See you at seven."

And with that Miriam curled up on the sofa and sobbed and sobbed. Something was telling her that Len wouldn't want this baby. But surely their love was greater than that? Had he not told her that he loved her in as many words? He wasn't married anymore. There was no reason why they couldn't marry. Surely, their love would transcend everything?"

Later that week they met at the restaurant as arranged. The restaurant was packed with couples, having a romantic evening together. The tone was subdued and intimate. There were candles and roses adorning every table. Champagne corks were popping. After exchanging polite small talk, Miriam could sense that Len suspected something was wrong.

"You don't appear your usual self darling. Is there something I have done to offend you?"

"Oh no, it's just that there is something I have to tell you and I don't think you'll feel like a champagne celebration when I've told you."

There was a long prolonged silence.

"I'm pregnant."

Len didn't respond. She stared at his cold expression, unable to read his face. His eyes were avoiding her gaze. He slowly took a sip of the champagne in front of him. Surely he felt something, anything?"

"I'm not ready for another child Miriam."

"Neither am I, I mean this is my first, but surely you don't want to get rid of it?" she whispered. "Our child."

"I will pay for everything you need Miriam. I will even pay for you to go to England, but I do not want this baby."

Miriam stared straight at him. Surely he felt some emotion, surely he couldn't just leave her to deal with this on her own?

Weren't these things up for negotiation? He made it seem so final. Tears were streaming down her face now. With whatever dignity she had left, she got up and left the restaurant. She ran down the street past Brown Thomas. She needed to get home to her apartment where she felt safe. She needed a drink. She passed many couples holding hands and kissing. This was how Len and her used to be. Not now.

She could hear footsteps behind her. She turned round and could see Len chasing her. Right now all she wanted was to get as far away from him as possible. Her feet carried her away faster and faster. All she could see ahead of her was oblivion. Somehow she managed to find her way back to the apartment. As she was struggling with the keys she could hear Len behind her.

"Miriam, let me help you with those."

"Not now." She spat " Happy Valentines Day."

And with that she opened and slammed the front door to her apartment behind her and curled up in a heap on the floor. Never had she loved so much and lost so much that evening. If only she could turn back the clock of time.

The following few days she just slept and slept. She couldn't bear the thought of going into work and phoned in sick. Her life was now officially a mess. She couldn't think straight. Thoughts of Len and his reaction haunted her. Every time the phone rang she wouldn't pick it up for fear it was him. Eventually she got a knock at the door.

"Who is it?"

"It's David. Can I come in?"

She slowly opened the door. Her kind friend had come to see her.

"You look awful! Darling we have been worried sick about you. Len told Pat you'd split up. Come here my pet."

And with that Miriam burst into tears and told him the details. David knew how to be discreet having remained steadfastly gay for many years.

"You do realize you'll have to get an illegal abortion." He said, handing her a warm brew of freshly made tea.

"But abortion can be so expensive and so dangerous David. What if I could never have children? You hear such terrible stories."

"I'm sure if you get the right doctor you'll be fine. Don't worry about the money. I can get a kitty going with the cast from the ballet. They are very discreet and they love you, you know."

"I need to get away from here and see my sister."

"Listen I'll lend you the money to help you get yourself sorted out. If you want my opinion he is behaving bastardly."

They talked and talked and talked that afternoon, drinking pints of tea. It was agreed that Miriam would tell her parents that she was going to England for a while, to pursue her career in fashion. They knew that, that was what she had set out to do. In the meantime she would stay with her sister. Her parents would know nothing about her pregnancy. David would meet up with Len and discuss his financial support.

"I don't think he should get off Scott free, do you?"

"He did offer, but I don't want to speak to him not just yet."

The following day she packed her bags with some bare essentials. Miriam was to take the Ferry from Dublin to Fishguard. From there she would take a train to London. The plan was, that she would stay with her sister and her husband and baby daughter in Muswell

Hill until she had made up her mind what to do. David came round and helped her pack. He gave her five hundred pounds that Len had given to take with her.

"There's more of that where that came from if you need it."

"I don't want his money David, don't you get it? I'd do anything for him to want me and the baby."

"Have you told your sis yet?"

"I couldn't bear to tell her on the phone. I'll tell her when I see her."

She gave him her sister's number and address in London and said her goodbyes.

"You know I will always be there for you. Take care with the termination."

With that she closed the door to her apartment in Dublin. The place that once held so many happy memories, was now tinted with sadness. She had had such huge ambitions to become a designer, to make something of her life. She was only in her twenties, at the pinnacle of her life. How had it gone so wrong? Now she had to face the consequences of her actions. Her sister had faced hers, now it was time for Miriam to face hers.

MARJORIE 1967
LONDON

NOW MARJORIE WAS so in love she could think of nothing more perfect than having a child with Arthur, the absolute embodiment of their love for each other. Arthur's job meant that Marjorie didn't have to work and so she could dedicate herself to being a full time mum. Although Arthur had had two sons from his previous marriage, he only got to see them every other weekend. By now Arthur and Marjorie were in their mid fifties and mid forties and they needed to crack on trying for a baby, if they were going to have any chance of living long enough to see their grand children. Not that such thoughts entered their minds as they still felt younger than their years. They felt that they had spent so much wasted time trying to find each other that they wanted to catch up on their lost youth.

Marjorie would take great pride in her appearance for Arthur's sake. They would catch every living moment to be together when he finished work. They would often laze about in the garden together in the afternoons on the weekends, rarely doing much except taking a leisurely lunch. It was like they had discovered love all over again.

For months and months they tried for a baby, but nothing

happened. Marjorie was forty-four years of age. She started to worry that the years of abuse to her body, by starving herself in her teens had taken a toll on her fertility. Her periods had stopped for one year when she was nineteen. She supposed that all her life, she had been in a state of semi anorexia.

One day she was sat in her next door neighbour's garden having a cool glass of lemonade. They were watching her children play in the sand pit, which her husband had constructed that weekend. Arthur wasn't due back until later. She bent down with a bucket to help one of the girls build a sand castle.

"So Marjorie, if you don't mind me asking, when are you thinking of having children? You and Arthur seem so happy together. It would be great to have some play mates for these two."

"You know what, I'd, we'd like nothing more. It hasn't been for want of trying. Unfortunately our biological clocks are not on our side."

"Nonsense. There are lots of women in their forties who have children, and healthy ones at that. I didn't conceive the twins until I was forty."

Marjorie stood up and came back to sit next to Jacqueline on the edge of the makeshift stone wall.

"What seems so unfair these days is everyone talking about the contraceptive pill and abortion, as if the new generation don't want to conceive. How can anyone think of killing a small baby?"

"I don't know Marjorie, but women want more choices now, to be able to choose when they want to have children and when they don't."

"I know, but I'd do anything to have Arthur's child. I don't care if it is handicapped, I would still love it as our own."

"Have you been to see a specialist yet?"

"Not yet. I guess I don't want to admit to being a failure. Arthur has had children. So nothing wrong in his department. What if I can never have children?"

Marjorie pulled at a blade of grass and gently twisted it around her fingers. She had to hold her breath slightly to stop the tears from coming. She was frightened to see a specialist in case they told her what she didn't want to hear.

"Don't be too hard on yourself. There are certain times of the month you can conceive more easily. You can tell by taking your temperature you know."

"It just makes it all sound so clinical. It's called making love, yet every day that goes past all I feel we're doing is making babies."

She knew if she was being honest with herself that when Arthur came home she was putting pressure on him. Probably all he wanted to do when he got home from work was sit down and relax in front of the television. She on the other hand was increasingly putting pressure on him to conceive a child. As if reading her thoughts Jacqueline intercepted.

"It won't hurt you know to go and see a specialist sooner rather than later. They may be able to give you some fertility treatment. I am sure Arthur would be supportive."

That evening she broached the subject with Arthur. They had just finished Question Time with Robin Day and were about to turn in for the evening. Arthur was sat in his favourite arm chair nursing a cup of coffee. She came and sat down beside him on a cushion on the carpet.

"I think it is time we saw a specialist."

"What for?" He said stroking her hair.

"I think we both know it hasn't been for want of trying, but I am not getting any younger and each month that goes by causes me more and more heart ache. What if I can't conceive?"

"You know I love you anyway, whether or not we have a baby."

"I know, but somehow the issue of having a baby has become all consuming to me. Only the other day I was walking down the street, and I know this sounds awful, but I see all these mums with babies and keep thinking I could be a good as mum as them."

"I think you would be a great mum."

"I feel so guilty for having left it so long. Do you think God is punishing me in some way?"

"No. Listen, we've only been trying for eighteen months. I'm a lot older now."

"It's me that needs checking out. We already know that you can have children."

The following day Marjorie made an appointment to see a specialist in Harley Street. The appointment was at lunchtime so that Arthur could meet her there in his lunch break. The specialist sent her to the Royal Free Hospital in Gray's Inn Road, to carry out various blood tests, and a scan of her fallopian tubes. On their return she handed the results to the doctor. They were told to wait outside in the waiting room whilst he formulated a prognosis.

"I'm scared. The scan itself was quite daunting."

"Don't get yourself in a fret. At least now we might get some answers."

They waited and waited for what seemed like an eternity. There were a number of other women in the waiting room. Some looked like single pregnant mothers, maybe contemplating an abortion. One woman in particular looked at Marjorie as if she could see the desperation in her face.

"Marjorie, the doctor will see you now."

She stood up slowly and holding Arthur's hand tightly entered the consultant's room in the corner. An elderly gentleman stood up to greet them. He had a kind face, etched with years of learning.

"Well, I won't keep you in suspense any longer. The good news is that there is no sign that your fallopian tubes are blocked."

"What does that mean doctor?"

"Well it means that if you were to conceive you are unlikely to suffer an ectopic pregnancy."

"The other good news is that your ovaries appear to be functioning normally, in that there appear to be no abnormalities."

"So why can't I get pregnant?"

"That's a good question. I suspect that in view of your age, that your ovaries are not producing as many eggs as you would like. This means it is harder for the sperm to get a chance as it were to hit the jackpot. Provided you watch your cycle carefully, I see no reason in the course of time why you shouldn't become pregnant."

"How long do we keep trying?"

"As long as it takes."

"Can't I take fertility drugs to make it happen sooner?" She enquired.

"I would advise against such treatment, unless you are prepared to risk a handicapped child."

The doctor explained that taking fertility drugs could result in a multiple pregnancy, and as these children were not conceived naturally there was a real danger that one or all of them would not survive. Even if they did survive they were predisposed to abnormality. Marjorie then asked about a new procedure she had heard of called in vitro fertilization, where they artificially inseminated the egg.

"That treatment, I'm afraid is not available yet and probably won't be available for many years to come, which in your case, bearing in mind your ages will be too late. Listen I suggest, in your case, you go back to the drawing board and enjoy the ride, in a manner of speaking. Come back and see me in a year."

They both smiled. Making babies was supposed to be fun. Maybe they had lost the plot a little. At least all the plumbing was in working order. Perhaps Marjorie's nerves and anxiety over the situation had got the better of her. Perhaps they should both relax a bit more.

The following months came and went. They spent many hours in the bedroom, but to no avail. Every time that time of the month came, she wept. Their love for each other grew and grew, but still no baby came. She would often see babies in the street and want to snatch them. Why did these mothers get a right to have a child when they didn't? She fantasized about having a baby growing inside her, willing it to happen to her, but it didn't. By the age of forty-five she realized it was almost impossible they were going to have their own child.

Their only option if they wanted one was to adopt one.

MIRIAM 1967
LONDON

WHEN MIRIAM ARRIVED in London, it was night time. She had been travelling all day and it had been exhausting. Her arms were strained from carrying the heavy luggage. Her clothes still smelt of the sea air from the ferry crossing. She arrived in Kings Cross station and caught the Northern Line to Muswell Hill. Her sister knew she was coming, as she had telephoned her the day before. She said she was going to prepare an irish stew for them to eat that evening as they wouldn't be able to go out with the young baby. As Miriam left the tube station she asked the man behind the flower stall for directions to Danvers Road.

"You need to follow this main road and then take a right. You will see the sign to Danvers Road on the wall. Have a good evening."

She followed the road as the man suggested. Danvers Road was a tree lined street of Edwardian terraced houses. There weren't many cars parked outside and the street was lit by low lit street lamps. When she arrived at 14 Danvers Road, she rang the doorbell. A man who she thought was the tenant for the ground floor flat, answered the door and pointed to a large blue door at the top of the stairs.

The passage was dark, as the light was not on. She walked up the stairs as her sister opened the door.

"Sis, I can't believe you're here! How are you?"

She ushered her inside and her put her bags on the floor. The flat was chaotic with baby bags and blankets and baby toys strewn across the floor. It was bright and clean though and had a nice homely feel. She could smell the irish stew from the kitchen. Patrick was stood behind her holding Charlotte. Miriam gave her sister a huge hug and her brother in law a kiss on the cheek and then bent down to kiss the baby.

"She's beautiful." Miriam said, visibly shaking with emotion. Her sister didn't suspect anything, just presumed she was caught up in the emotion of meeting her niece for the first time. She looked so tiny still, so delicate, her smell as sweet as powder.

"You must be exhausted sis. Come and sit down and have a drink with us. Patrick is just going to settle Charlotte down and then we can have a good old gossip. It's been so long."

Miriam took off her jacket and sat herself down on the small sofa just under the window. The street light radiated through the window, casting a shadow over the small dining table laid for three. Her sister had photos of all the family, including their mum and dad on the mantelpiece. There was a small fireplace under the mantelpiece which had some logs burning in it. It reminded Miriam of the peat fires they would have in Ireland. Above the photos, hung a Brigid's cross. This was an Irish habit of her sisters' who would hang this cross up to protect her from evil spirits. She heard her sister clanking about with various pots and pans in the kitchen.

"Do you need any help there sis?" Miriam asked.

"No, you're alright. I'll bring the drinks through in a minute."

"Smells good," said Patrick as he walked back into the living room. They both looked tired. Perhaps it was the stress of looking after the baby that was getting them down. She knew her sister was thinking about going back to work soon. She knew they needed the money, but she didn't agree with the notion of a woman going to work and leaving their baby behind. It was for this reason, she couldn't dream of becoming a single mother. She would have to work to feed her baby. It didn't bear thinking about. Patrick sat down on the sofa beside her and gave her a hug.

"You look dead beat girl."

"I am. I don't like the ferry at the best of times. The crossing was quite rough today across that Irish Sea."

"Here you are sis. I've made us all whisky macs. It should perk us up a bit. Hopefully Charlotte will sleep for another six hours if we are lucky. We're trying to settle her into a routine, but it isn't easy."

"What's it like having the new edition?" Miriam asked.

"Oh it's chaotic. It's turned our lives upside down, but we wouldn't have it any other way would we Patrick? They don't tell you about the sleepless nights or about the whole horrendous childbirth thing. I don't know why mum didn't warn me. Still she gets stronger every day. You just focus, all your attentions on the baby, nothing else matters."

The fire was crackling away now and Patrick stood up to put another log on. You could smell the fire emanating through the room, and hear the hum of the traffic from the main road in the distance. Miriam took a sip from the whisky which was ice cold, the large cubes clinking against the tumbler. Patrick went to the kitchen and opened a bottle of wine. The popping of the cork was strangely comforting.

"So, how easy have you found it to get work down here? I've got to get a job soon."

"Well Patrick got a job fairly easily with a building firm. The property market is booming at the moment. For us, you can always get a job in Harrods, but the pay is lousy and the staff are not very nice."

"I was thinking of getting some modelling work to tie me over. I thought I'd pop down to Lucie Clayton and some of the modelling agencies they referred us to, see what I can get. I will pay my way you know. It was very kind of you to offer to put me up, what with the baby and all."

"Oh it was nothing sis. Anyway we could do with a helping hand, particularly at nights if I'm to start work again. I don't have a choice."

But you do have a choice, Miriam thought. Patrick is supporting you, bringing the money in. Charlotte should have her mother there, holding her, nurturing her, willing her to grow. How sad that Miriam couldn't have that option. Len didn't want this baby or her, for that matter. She had some very difficult decisions to make. She had resolved to talk about it later, maybe when Patrick went off for a pint later at the local pub.

"Supper should be ready now. That's what I like about irish stew, it practically cooks by itself."

With that Orla got up and donned an apron. She took the stew out of the oven and brought it to the table. They sat down and Orla asked them to help themselves from the pot. Then she brought the beans and more gravy and put them in the middle of the table with the stew, whilst Patrick poured the wine. The fire continued to crackle. In the distance they could hear a number of sirens blaring. This was the London, Miriam remembered, when she was studying at St Martin's Lane.

"Funny to think dad came from London. He doesn't talk about it much. I think he thinks it will offend mum."

"Oh I don't know sis. He often mentions his childhood. I think it was more difficult for him, because he was here during the war. He was too old for service being twenty five years older than mum."

Her sister and Patrick didn't mention Len during that dinner. They knew they had split up, but Miriam thought her sister knew it was a painful subject and best dealt with when no men were present. Miriam was grateful for that. When they had finished eating, Orla went to check on Charlotte.

"She's sound asleep thank goodness. Now we can relax."

"I think I'll pop round to the local for a pint of guinness, if that's alright with you girls. I'm sure you have some catching up to do."

"You go. We'll be fine," said Orla.

Miriam was grateful to Patrick for giving them this time together. If the baby woke in the day they would be interrupted. It would be far easier to talk whilst she was sound asleep in the evening. Orla put on a record by Dusty Springfield and turned down the volume so that it was just in the background. Orla sat on the floor and Miriam sat on the sofa.

They waited for the front door to slam, then Orla passed Miriam her glass of wine and offered her a cigarette. Miriam hesitated.

"I shouldn't really be having one of these."

"Why not? It's never stopped you before."

A silence hung in the air. She could hear the cog wheels of her sister's brain turning round. To hell with it, why shouldn't she have a cigarette? She couldn't be in any worse a position than she was already in? In any event, was she going to keep the baby?

"Go on then."

They lit their cigarettes and both took a sip of wine.

"Are you going to tell me what is going on sis? I mean you split up with the love of your life, jack in a fairly decent job with prospects and hop it to London. You normally plan things."

"Not this time sis."

"What do you mean?"

She paused, trying to take in the enormity of it all, how quickly this had all happened. She felt so alone, yet she had her sister with her and the child she was carrying. How different her life had seemed a few weeks ago. How everything had changed. The fire had stopped crackling now and just sizzled with a quiet ember.

"I'm pregnant sis. I didn't mean to be, I mean I didn't plan it this way, but I was so in love, or thought I was. He doesn't want it. He doesn't want a child, a child with me."

The hopelessness of her situation, overcame her and she burst in to uncontrollable sobs. Orla took the cigarette off her and hugged and rocked her until the inconsolable crying had subsided. Her eyes were puffy and red now, and sore, with the sheer stress of it all.

"Surely he will come round? It is not as if he hasn't had children before, even been married before. Have you tried talking to him?"

"There's no point. I could see it in his eyes. He offered me money to get rid of it. With him it is matter of fact. I don't know what to do sis. Our parents would kill us if they knew. They must never know about this baby. Will you promise me that sis, on your baby's life?"

"Yes of course, of course, but what ARE you going to do about this baby? Sooner or later, you will start showing. I can't keep this from Patrick forever. If you are going to have an abortion, you need to get it done sooner rather than later, because after a certain period there is no going back!"

Her sister was clearly agitated now, anxious for her and her well being, anxious for all of them.

"I feel terrible about lying about this to our parents, but what can we do. My hormones are all over the place. I feel incapable of making any rational decisions right now. All I know, is this baby was conceived out of love and now that love has gone. The thought of going through an abortion is tearing me apart, but what else can I do? I can't afford to look after myself, let alone bring up a child as a single parent. My whole world has fallen apart sis."

Miriam threw her face into her hands and Orla lit her another cigarette.

"Listen, I know this has come as a bit of a shock to you and you haven't had time to rationalize anything, but don't you think you have been a bit hasty about Len. I mean only two months ago you were having fabulous weekends away. I mean he is older than us, certainly a lot more responsible than my Patrick, surely he won't shirk responsibility for this. I just don't fecking believe it!"

She knew what her sister was saying, but it was no use. She knew that look of utter disdain, she had seen that evening on Valentine's Day. If only she hadn't seen it.

"What's it like giving birth sis?" Miriam said, trying to change the subject "Is it as bad as you said?"

"Oh you don't want to go there sis at the moment. Let's just work out what you are going to do with this baby. Have you got any money? I mean, for an abortion?"

"Oh don't worry, Len is sorting out that side of things. I can still get a job, until I start showing. David is doing a whip round at his local gay bar. They obviously have no reason to let the cat out of the bag."

"Are you thinking about an abortion?"

"I honestly don't know sis. When I saw your baby today, all sorts of emotions came flooding in. She is just so helpless and vulnerable and alive. How can I think of killing such a thing!"

Her thoughts had been a mess when she had first seen and smelt Charlotte. She now had a living baby inside her. It may just be a blob, but it was her blob, that would one day turn into a life if she let it.

"I know you haven't decided what to do sis, but I know a friend who went to see a specialist in Harley Street. They put her on to a reputable doctor, nothing legal of course, who carried out, you know, the evacuation procedure. It wouldn't harm you to see them if you have the money."

"I can't make any decisions right now, I'm exhausted sis."

"How about I make you a nice cup of cocoa and put you to bed before Patrick comes home. It's normally a late one, if he meets his

Irish mates. I'll warm up a hot water bottle to take to bed with you."

With that she dispatched Miriam up another flight of stairs to the bedroom in the attic. She snuggled into bed with her cocoa and hot water bottle and started to doze off. She was awoken a few hours later with a front door slamming and the sound of Patrick bumping into furniture in the dark. The baby began to cry and she heard her sister scalding Patrick for waking the baby. There was a clash of dishes in the kitchen as her sister could be heard warming, she supposed a milk bottle to feed Charlotte. Was she ready for this she thought? Her eyes were drooping, willing her to go back to sleep. Eventually she fell in to a deep slumber, too exhausted to care.

After an exhausting week at her sister's house, she walked one day, down to the end of Danvers Road, armed with a telephone number for some specialist in Harley Street. When she reached the phone box, she checked there was no one else waiting, and took the piece of paper out of her hand bag and rang the number. The phone rang three times, before a receptionist with a clipped accent answered.

"Harley Street Obstetric Clinic, can I help you?"

"I would like to book an appointment."

"To see whom?"

"I don't know."

"Well, can you give me an indication?" she said some what exacerbated.

"All I know is, it is something your clinic specializes in."

"May I ask, are you pregnant?"

Miriam paused, she did not want to admit that she was pregnant to a stranger on the telephone, it seemed somehow so impersonal.

She could hear a sigh on the other end of the telephone. The street was quiet and she checked to see that no one was around to hear their conversation. After a long pause she whispered.

"I understand that you have a doctor who can cure menstrual blockages."

"We do."

"Then can I make that appointment?"

" I suggest I make an appointment for you with Doctor Marsden on Thursday at 4 o'clock prompt. Our fees are £50 cash per consultation. Your name please?"

"Oh er Mrs Smith."

" Doesn't sound very Irish, considering your accent."

"Oh I married an Englishman," she said thinking on her feet.

"Very well, we will see you on Thursday."

When Thursday came, she put on a smart cream dress and a small tailored jacket and took the tube to Oxford Circus. She took a brisk walk up Regent Street and then took a left into New Cavendish Street and started to look out for the sign for Harley Street. The piece of paper had the number 95 written on it and she scanned the street for the even and odd numbers and realized she needed to turn right. The entrance to the building was imposing with a large black door and a brass buzzer. There were lots of suited men in bowler hats, walking in both directions. She pressed the buzzer and the door opened with a click.

She approached the haughty woman sitting behind her desk, at reception.

"I have an appointment to see a Doctor Marsden."

"Mrs Smith I assume." She said raising her eyebrow.

"Yes."

"Take a seat over there and a nurse will come and take you to the doctor shortly."

Miriam took a seat in one of the large leather sofas. She could see that there were about two or three other ladies before her. One was heavily pregnant and looked as if she were about to give birth. Another had a small baby with her, not much older than Charlotte. There was also a rather miserable looking woman in her forties with her husband. Perhaps she was here because she couldn't conceive. How Miriam longed to swap places with her.

She picked up one of the expensive magazines amongst the Vogues and Tatlers on the table. The receptionist brought her a cup of coffee with a bowl of sugar and a jug of milk, made out of what looked like expensive china. The room was silent as the baby was sleeping. Everyone was lost in their own thoughts. She took two sugar cubes from the bowl and stirred them in to her coffee. The room was dominated by a very grand ornate fireplace with a gilt edged mirror above it, much grander than the one at the surgery in Dublin.

Her thoughts went back to the catholic school her sister and her had attended as a child. It had been a very strict convent school on the outskirts of Macroom. The nuns had looked after them and fussed over them, but it was an extremely catholic upbringing with mass every morning and evening. Their religious teacher had been a priest who had spent hours and hours talking about how bad abortion was. He had shown their twelve-year-old eyes pictures of aborted babies, and he would yell at the top of his lungs in class, how wrong it was to kill an innocent life. Every time she thought of this baby, a picture of this priest popped in to her head as it did now. It was as if he knew, now ten years on, that Miriam would be sitting in this surgery, in Harley Street, thinking about aborting this baby.

She caught the eye of the receptionist who was looking at her with disdain. She's thinking she hasn't got a wedding ring so she must be dirty or unclean. She had stupidly overseen this small detail. She hung her head in shame and returned to the magazine she was reading. It talked about contraception and the fact that soon the family planning clinics in England would be offering contraception in England. If only she'd had access to contraception and not relied on the catholic rhythm method. Her life would be so different now.

"Mrs Smith, the doctor will see you now," a nurse said, tapping her shoulder. She led her down a series of corridors until they came to a door with Doctor Marsden's plaque on it. She knocked the door.

"Come in."

Miriam entered a room to find a male doctor standing quite formally behind his mahogany desk. The room was full of antiques with an ornate chandelier hanging in the middle of the room. He was wearing a suit with a jacket slung over the back of his chair. She guessed he was in his mid forties, with slightly receding hair. His eyes were dark brown and his skin was slightly tanned.

"Nurse, you may leave us now. We're not to be disturbed." The nurse slowly clicked the door behind her.

"Right, Mrs Smith, just to dispense with some formalities, I take it your name is not Mrs Smith?"

"No, sir."

"You are about twenty four years of age and that you have come to me about a pregnancy?"

"Yes."

"That you are not married and want to consider your options?"

"Yes."

"Where are you currently residing?"

"I've come from Ireland, but I am staying at my sister's place in Muswell Hill."

"I take it that you have sufficient funds?"

"Yes I do, or rather, my partner has. He has offered to pay for everything."

"I assume you are here, because there are no solutions for you in Ireland?"

"Yes."

The doctor leaned back in his expensive leather chair and clasped his hands together. He swivelled the chair slightly to look out of the window and then swivelled back again. A silence hung in the room, whilst he appeared to be in quite serious thought. Miriam noticed a photo in a silver frame of a woman and two children, who she presumed to be his family. How lovely to be so happy and in love with your wife and so settled, she thought.

"Mrs Smith, or can I call you by your first name?"

"Miriam."

"Miriam, I don't have to tell you this, as you probably know, but abortion, if that is the road you are going down, is still illegal in this country. It carries a life sentence and whilst mothers are rarely prosecuted they are sometimes imprisoned, if found out.

There may be talk, this year of David Steele the MP introducing the Abortion Act, but even if this were to go through this would not be enacted until April 1968, the earliest, which doesn't help you one iota. You can still carry out the abortion yourself or have what is called a back-street abortion. Such a decision should not be taken lightly I might add. I can tell you, I do consultancy work at St Mary's Hospital Paddington and I see five to ten cases a day of women with pain and bleeding from early pregnancy, often or not caused from early abortions."

The doctor paused to gauge her reaction. He picked up a silver pen and twiddled it between his fingers, all the time watching her. The clock on the mantelpiece timed on the half hour.

"If you decided to go for the back-street option, you are taking a number of risks. There have been some reports of lead poisoning, but I would say that anyone that offers you these products, is not qualified to take out the procedure."

He then ripped a piece of paper off his pad and started to draw a triangle.

"This represents your uterus, and this is where your foetus lies at the moment. There are essentially two procedures that can be carried out under supervision, one is surgical abortion, by vacuum aspiration or dilation and the other is curettage. I'll explain."

Miriam pulled her chair a little closer to look at the diagram. She made a nervous cough, looking at the drawing. They were discussing a baby here, a baby that was inside her.

"Slow me down if I am getting too technical. Vacuum aspiration involves dilating the cervix. The uterine contents, in your case the foetus is withdrawn by the means of a small tube, called a cannula which is connected to a vacuum pump or hand operated syringe. Dilation or curettage is when a curette or spoon tipped metal instrument, in layman's language is used to dislodge the foetus."

He then paused and leant back in his chair again. The rain was beginning to pour outside and tap against the window pane. The doctor got up and walked to the surgical white bed with metal bars in the corner of the room. He went to the sink, to wash his hands and then wiped his hands on the towel. He then patted the bed and said

"I suggest I examine you. How many weeks pregnant are you?"

"About eight weeks." She said as she approached the bed.

"Just take your jacket and shoes off and lie down for me."

He then took a stethoscope and placed it on her heart. He then undid the buttons on her dress and placed the small round disc on her stomach. He then took her arm and placed a blood pressure monitor on it. He slowly inflated the bag and took her pulse, pumping it with the small contraption underneath.

"Mum and baby are doing fine." He said. He then beckoned her to get down from the bed and back to the desk.

"I have a question to ask." She said.

"Go on."

"If having an abortion is illegal, then how can you help me?"

"Let me just say, that in return for a large fee, there are ways, we doctors can interpret the law, that in a way, allows us to terminate pregnancies. This information must not, you understand, leave these four walls and you should always refer to your problem as a menstrual blockage amongst friends."

"Yes, yes, I completely understand."

The doctor got up and proceeded to the bookshelf to retrieve a large leather bound book. He returned to the desk and flipped through a number of pages.

"It says here that if a doctor were to assess that continuing the pregnancy for the mother will make the mother a mental and physical wreck then the doctor will be preserving the life of the mother and so make the abortion legal."

"Yes, but I am not a mental and physical wreck."

"Ah but that is down to interpretation and it is a matter for me to assess whether your life needs preserving on this occasion."

"Would you carry out the procedure here?"

"Good Heavens no, I would make a referral to two Harley Street psychiatrists in Half Moon Street and then the abortion would be carried out in Ealing under their instruction. In other words, I would have to get two psychiatrists to say you were upset enough and then you would stay overnight in a north London clinic. I have to say Miriam, this is not for the faint hearted. You may never be able to have children again, although it is still possible. Anything can be achieved, if you have money."

Miriam sat and pondered what he had just told her. She was not ready to make a decision yet. She'd only just got used to the idea of being pregnant. To call it a foetus, inside of her, was to dehumanize it. It was a baby and this doctor had heard its' heartbeat. Those pictures that priest had shown her at school, kept flashing back in her head.

"Listen, you don't have to make a decision now. How about I hand you a letter of referral to the Half Moon Street specialists, I talked about. At least you have then gone away with something for your consultation fee. There will be no need to come back and see me, unless, you decide to keep the baby of course."

She nodded and the doctor picked up his pen and began to write the letter of referral. He blotted the piece of paper with some blotting paper and then neatly folded it and put it in an envelope and sealed it for her.

"I hope you find it in your heart to make the right decision Miriam. Good Luck."

With that they shook hands and Miriam left the office. She found her way back down the various corridors, back to reception. The receptionist looked up and noticed her clutching the letter of referral to her chest. Her eyes rolled slightly as she fidgeted about her desk.

"That will be £50 please."

Miriam opened her purse and took out the notes. That would leave her with £450, unless Len was prepared to lend her more.

"Do you require a receipt?"

"No thanks." Miriam said.

The receptionist raised an eyebrow and proceeded to buzz open the front door for her. Outside, it was raining quite hard now. She took a small umbrella out from her handbag and put it up to shield her hair and clothes from the rain. Taxis raced by splashing her shoes as she hurried towards the train station. Oh sod it, she thought, this has been a hard day, so she hailed a cab to the tube.

Back at the flat in Danvers Road, Miriam started to prepare the tea for when Orla came home. She had bought some gammon from the butchers on the way back from the tube station and had decided to make one of their favourites, roast gammon with parsley sauce and colcannon potatoes, pure Irish comfort food. The television was on in the background with the news.

"The US spacecraft Surveyor 3 which was launched this month, soft lands on the moon today, where it conducts sampling experiments on lunar soil."

The front door slammed and she heard Orla come up the stairs. She had Charlotte on her hips and was soaking wet from the rain.

"How was it today sis?" She said slightly out of breath.

"Oh, so so."

Orla put Charlotte down in the baby chair and glanced at the television. The smell of gammon was starting to permeate through the flat.

"Good God, they'll be landing people on the moon next."

"Fancy a drink sis, I was just about to open a bottle of wine?"

"Sure, make mine a large one."

Miriam knew she shouldn't be drinking in her condition, but somehow, if she carried on drinking and smoking, maybe the decision would be made for her and she would naturally miscarry. In any event, most of their family had drunk through their pregnancies. They figured if their ancestors had existed on ale alone, they hadn't come to much harm as a result of it. She just wasn't prepared to make any sacrifices just yet. The enormity of carrying a child inside of her and the stress of seeing beautiful Charlotte sat before her was too much to bear. She grabbed a bottle of wine from the fridge and opened it. She then poured them two large glasses.

"Patrick has gone to the pub. Don't think he will be back until late."

"I hope he doesn't feel squeezed out by me being here. I don't want to come between you two you know. You have enough to cope with as it is with the little un."

"Oh no sis, we wouldn't be without you. You're my sis. If you save him some tea, you'll win his heart. You can always get to a man through his stomach as mum would say. Listen, I'm going to feed Charlotte and then I'll put her down for her sleep. Then we can have a good old chat."

Orla picked up Charlotte and took her to her bedroom to feed her, where it was quieter. Miriam checked on the gammon to see that it was roasting nicely and then plonked herself in front of the television. The rain was still pelting outside. It felt cosy in that flat. There was something on the news about "All you need is love" being the greatest song of all time. Apparently the Beatles had released a new album called "Sergeant Pepper's Lonely Hearts Club Band". How she longed to go out and do all the things they used to do like going to night clubs.

"I don't suppose you've seen my cigarettes anywhere? Oh there they are." She sat down next to Miriam and lit a cigarette.

"It is such a relief when you finally get time to yourself. They are so dependent on you at this age, it is exhausting. To be honest, it is taking its' toll on Patrick. I'm going to have to get some work soon."

"I don't mind looking after Charlotte, if you want to go back to work sis."

"You can't possibly in your condition. You've got too much on your mind at the moment sis."

"I'd like to."

"What brought this on?"

"I went to see that Harley Street doctor today, you know, the one your friend recommended. I just don't know sis, whether I can go through with all this? I know I don't want to be a single mother, but I don't think I can bear to be responsible for killing a child."

"It's not a child at the moment, Miriam, it's just a foetus."

"That's what the doctor kept referring to, but when he listened to its' heartbeat, he referred to it as a baby and me a mother. Don't I owe this child a responsibility now that I have made it? Good God I would like nothing better than for Len to come back to me and say, sorry, all is forgiven. Surely he wouldn't want me to go through an abortion with what I've heard today. There is a risk, that if I go through with it that I might not be able to have any more children. I have heard some horrific stories that women can even die from these back street abortions."

"I thought if you had the money, they weren't back street."

"Oh you pay the money to legalize it, but it is still back street."

The more and more Miriam thought about it, the more she realized the risk she was taking. She hadn't spoken to Len, not properly, her pride had stood in the way of all that. Maybe he was just testing her, seeing if she would go through with it and abort her own child. As if reading her own thoughts, Orla suggested.

"Maybe you should call him? Let him know how you feel. Maybe he will come round."

Miriam put her head in to her hands. She didn't even know, if Len was still in Ireland. For all she knew he had gone back to South Africa or may be he was in London. She couldn't bear to go chasing him around to find out where he was. She'd left no forwarding address or number. He probably thought she no longer cared.

"What sort of mess have I got myself in to sis? I don't know where to start."

Her sister said she would look after the tea and that Miriam should go down to the phone box and phone him. Someone was bound to know where he was. She couldn't make any rational decisions until she'd spoken to him. She put on her shoes and coat and took an umbrella. The street was awash with water as she hurried along to the telephone box. She could see all the lights on in the houses and flats as she passed. Families having supper with their children after a long day at work, getting ready for the new start the next day. When she got to the phone box, she inserted the coins and began dialing the only number she had for Len in Ireland. The phone rang a number of times and to her surprise a woman answered.

"Could I speak to Leonard Jackson please?"

"Just one moment, Len!" she could hear her shouting "There is a lady on the phone wanting to speak to you." She then asked Miriam to hold on while he picked up the phone in his study. The phone clicked and Len came on the line.

"How are you?" she said after a pause. She did not know whether this other woman was listening in on the telephone line.

"I'm fine and you?"

"OK." But she wasn't OK, she was far from OK. Didn't he realize how difficult it was for her to make this call? She wanted him to say he missed her, that he loved her and that he was sorry that he had hurt her.

"I can't go through with this."

"Well that is up to you. You know my decision."

"Does everything have to be so final with you? Don't you have an ounce of care in you? I've done as you asked. I went to see somebody. I just can't do it."

"I love you Miriam, very, very much. I don't have room for two of you."

The phone pips went beep, beep, beep, asking her to put more money in. She scrambled round in the dark, but couldn't find any more change and the phone just went dead. She dropped the receiver leaving it hanging by its' wire and banged the phone with her fist.

"Damn you Len, damn you." She started to sob. It was no use phoning again. She would get David to speak to him next time. It was time to start making her own decisions, for her and her baby. She slowly walked back to the flat. Orla was laying the table when Miriam got back.

"Any luck sis?"

"I don't want to talk about it."

"Come and sit down and have something to eat."

"You eat sis. I'm not hungry. I'll keep you company though."

Finally Miriam told her about her conversation with Len and the fact he didn't want to know. Part of her was consumed with jealousy over the fact that a woman had answered the phone. Her sister said that they couldn't resolve these issues until they'd seen each other and talked it through. If Len was made to understand how dangerous abortion was then may be he would reconsider things. After dinner they sat down on the sofa and poured themselves another couple of glasses of wine.

"What will you do if you decide to keep the baby?" Her sister asked.

"I don't know. I couldn't afford to bring it up without working and I don't agree with the idea of a working mother. No offence to you sis, but we have different views on the matter. In any event mum and dad would never speak to me again."

"How about we consider if I should have it?"

"Sis, I couldn't do that to you. The child would end up growing up with you and calling you "Mummy" and I couldn't bear that. How could we explain it all to mum and dad and everybody. It just doesn't feel right."

There was a short silence, whilst they both paused in thought. If abortion and being a single mother was not an option, then what was? Neither of them wanted to discuss that option.

"You could always consider putting the baby up for adoption."

And with that and a heavy heart they said their "goodnights" and went to bed.

MARJORIE 1967
LONDON

NOW ARTHUR AND Marjorie had decided that their only option was to adopt a baby, they started to make tentative enquiries. The Local Borough Council suggested they contact, The National Adoption Society, The Church of England Children's Society, The National Children's Adoption Association, The National Children's Home and Dr Barnado's to name a few.

The National Adoption Society asked if they had been divorced as this might require a special interview. In fact they never got to the interview stage.

"Thank you for your letter. I am afraid, however, that we cannot help you as we only place very young babies for adoption and, because of this, have an age limit of forty for adopters. I would suggest that you apply to one of the large children's homes to adopt a toddler or slightly older child."

"I don't believe this!" she exclaimed to Arthur over breakfast that morning.

"What allows them to make the assumption that once you are over forty you are past it to look after children?"

"Calm down love. They have to make some rules."

"Yes, but with you being in your fifties we have no hope."

"I doubt very much they care about my age, as long as I bring in the income."

Marjorie started to riffle through the various leaflets that she had collected from the library. She had assumed that adoption would be easy for them. They were married and lived in a three bedroom, two reception roomed house with all the modern cons and a garden and a garage. Arthur earned £2500 a year before tax as a chemical engineer. They were nothing short of ideal parents.

She slowly scanned the leaflet from Dr Barnado's whilst sipping on her cup of coffee. Arthur was tucking in to a slice of toast.

"It says here that Dr Barnado's aim is to choose adopters, who will be good parents, who will bestow upon the child such love and care as will ensure its normal development, physically, mentally and spiritually, and who will by their example and teaching help the child grow up as a Christian. Arthur I know we can be all these things to a baby, our baby."

"Yes darling, I am sure we can, but what are the prohibitive criteria."

"Well, let me see. It says they will only consider married couples who are between the ages of the 25 and 40 if they wish to adopt a YOUNG baby. So we could always adopt an older baby. Oh no wait, it says here that couples wishing to adopt older children should not be more than forty years older than the children they wish to adopt."

"Well I can't see how we are going to get round this one. List me some more criteria, just the prohibitive ones."

"Married couples with a marked difference in age. Does the fact that I'm 44 and you are 54 count as a marked age difference?"

"Go on."

"Married couples who have a poor health record. Well neither of us have that, and lastly members of the Roman Catholic Church, because they make there own arrangements for adoption. May be we should approach the Catholic Church?"

"How many children do Dr Barnado's homes have?"

"It says here that they have about 7,000 children in the care of the homes, but very few of these are admitted for adoption. Many are in care for temporary periods only; others will ultimately be restored to their families; some are happily in close touch with various members of their own family; some are severely handicapped."

"Who initiates the adoption process, if there are so few adoptions?" Arthur asked pouring himself another coffee.

"According to this leaflet, adoption plans are initiated at the mother's request, and they do all they can to ensure that she has definitely decided on adoption before the child is placed. She has however, the right under the Adoption Act to change her mind at any time until an adoption order is made. In certain exceptional circumstances the Court may dispense with the mother's consent."

Marjorie could see Arthur mulling this all over. He took another slice of toast from the toast rack and started to spread it with a thin film of butter.

"It seems to me that the only way we are going to be able to adopt a child is some how to make an arrangement with a mother before she enters the legal process. I don't know how regular that might be and it may even be unlawful."

"Our problem is that time is not on our side. It says in most of these leaflets that it can take twelve months to find a placement.

Not only that, even if they were to place a child with us which now seems increasingly unlikely, we would have to get satisfactory medical reports and then go through a probationary period with the social workers. It says here we would need at least three satisfactory references. One referee should be a minister of religion, another should be a woman, if possible one who is either a mother or who has some experience in the care of children and who has known the applicants for several years. Arthur, I don't have any experience with children. I only started wanting a baby when I met you!"

"Perhaps we could arrange an appointment with Doctor Langdon. He may know who to approach. He has also known me for many years."

The following morning they went to see him at his small surgery in High Barnet. It was a Saturday, so the surgery was not full and they were led straight through to his offices. He confirmed that their age was unfortunately a problem, but that he fully empathized with them having followed their strenuous efforts to conceive a child of their own. He had a good relationship with the local child care officer, and would make some tentative enquiries.

That week, they tried to carry on as normal desperately waiting for a phone call from the doctor. That call came on the Thursday evening when he said he had spoken to the child care officer who had a baby on the Panel, but when she had heard that they were both over forty and divorcees she could not put their names forward. Apparently the local judge had a strong prejudice against divorcees. He had however two more panel babies for adoption, one already born and one expected in March. He said he had asked a child care officer he knew, not the local one, about fostering and she told him that a couple can become foster parents to a child, through a doctor, called a third party without informing the child care officer. The only person who could upset things was the natural mother and the doctor said that he thought that highly unlikely in either of these cases.

Arthur and Marjorie were ecstatic when they put the phone down.

"I think we should see a solicitor right away to check it is all legal." Arthur said.

"Yes, but Arthur, we are no longer talking about adoption, but fostering. I have always been under the impression that foster parents have practically no rights. I thought we were looking for a permanent arrangement?"

"Calm down let's see what the solicitor says. Why don't you write to him."

The following week Marjorie received a letter from the solicitor Hirst & Capes:-

Hirst & Capes

London EC4

Dear Mrs Ronson

I am in receipt of your letter of the 3rd of February. I sympathize with yourself and your husband very much in the difficulty in which you find yourselves as to the possible adoption of a child.

I am a little worried about the possible arrangements which your Doctor has in mind for the following reasons:-

1. *It seems to me the child would come under part IV of the Adoption Act 1958. Under this it is the duty of those arranging such a matter to notify the Local Authority to see that children in this position are visited from time to time by Officers of Authority, who are to satisfy themselves as to the wellbeing of the child.*

2. *Quite apart from this, you would have no legal standing so far as the child is concerned. The mother could, at any time, have the child back, if she wished. You say that this is considered to be unlikely, but one is often coming across cases where this happens, however unlikely it seemed to be at the time; in such case you would have no legal standing in the matter whatsoever. If it did happen, it could result in very considerable distress to yourself and to your husband, and quite possibly to the child.*

3. *I should add here, simply as a footnote, that if you did go through with such an arrangement, it would be essential for you and your husband to consider your Wills, and to make specific arrangements therein for the child as you might wish, as otherwise the child would have no rights.*

I note that you feel the difficulty is the County Court Judge, in that he holds very strong views in such matters in regard to persons who have been divorced. What I am wondering is whether it would not be practicable, in the circumstances of this new child, to make the application to the Magistrates instead of to the Judge. The Magistrates equally have Jurisdiction on these matters. In either case, whether it be the Judge or Magistrates, they have to consider whether the proposed adoption is in the best interests of the child, and it might be that the Magistrates would not take the same view about an adoption by people who have been previously divorced as the Judge does. You cannot, of course re-apply to the Magistrate in the case which has already been decided by the Judge, but I do not see why the new case could not be put before the Magistrates, who may well have different views on what after all is purely a matter of practical opinion, and not a matter of law.

I know nothing as to any particular mystic affect of the age of forty!

To summarize, therefore, I should be very reluctant to see you enter into any informal arrangement, for the reasons I have given above; but I do not see why you should not try again for a formal adoption before the Magistrates, and in which respect you might, with advantage, consult a local solicitor.

With Kind Regards

Mr Thompson

"He doesn't sound very encouraging." Marjorie said.

"Perhaps we should go back and talk to Mrs Barnet the Senior Child Care Officer. See if there are any other options?"

"There are no other options. If Doctor Langdon cannot help us through the back door, then who else can? Even if we find a child they won't let us legally adopt her. We don't fit the criteria."

Marjorie could see that her anguish was causing stress to Arthur, but she so wanted them to be complete to have a child they could nurture together and bring up on their own. She could see now that any attempt to have their own child would be thwarted by the authorities. They would have a life of social services at their back door. What had they done to deserve this she wondered?

MIRIAM 1967
LONDON

THE IDEA OF giving up a baby for adoption was alien to Miriam. The very thought of taking a pregnancy to full term, giving it up and then giving it to someone else you didn't know, with no contact seemed incomprehensible. She didn't have the resources to look after a child but what qualified someone else? What if she gave up this child and it ended in a Dr Barnado's children's home?

Miriam decided that she needed to know a little more about the process of adoption, so the following day she put on her coat and headed for the local library in Muswell Hill on the High Street. She could feel the cold wind chapping against her cheeks, as she hurried towards the entrance. Inside the library it smelt of books old and new. There was a rather prim and proper lady sitting at the reception doing the filing. There was a quiet hush, despite the loud thunder of traffic outside.

"Can I help you miss?"

"Could you tell me where the public section is, the section where you keep leaflets?" She asked.

"Straight down the far left aisle, at the end. If you need any assistance, just ask."

Miriam gingerly went down the far aisle and found the section where all the papers and pamphlets were. They were arranged in alphabetical order. She ran her finger down the "A" section and stumbled on a leaflet titled "The National Adoption Society Leaflet Information". She pulled a chair up to a small booth and sat down and read its' contents.

"Adoption is a way of providing a child with new legal parents. It ends the legal relationship between birth parents and establishes a new one with the adoptive parents. Adoptions are arranged by adoption agencies, but are made legally binding by the Courts. Once granted, an Adoption Order is final and cannot be undone."

Miriam turned to the back of the leaflet and there were a number of recommended agencies and social workers to contact. The one that drew her attention was the Golder's Green Adoption Agency in the Finchley Road. She took the leaflet and stuffed it in her clutch bag, checking around her, to see that no one was looking. She then left the library through the turnstiles and headed for the nearest bus stop. When the bus came, she headed to the front of the bus and took a seat in the corner. She then took out the leaflet and checked the address, 274 Finchley Road. She got off at the bus stop near the tube station and headed northwards, counting the numbers as she went. The entrance to the agency was above a charity shop, up a small flight of stairs.

"How can I help?" said a woman standing in the doorway. Miriam guessed she was in her fifties, quite smartly dressed, with her hair swept back into a scarf.

"I've come to speak to someone about adoption."

"Take a seat."

Miriam sat down and straightened her skirt. The office was very bland with a small window to the left overlooking the Finchley Road. There were a few books on the bookshelf about adoption and childbirth. The lady in the doorway, closed the door whilst changing the sign to "Interview in Progress" before sitting down opposite her.

"I take it you have come to talk to me about giving a child up for adoption?"

"Yes."

"What would you like to know?"

"Well I've never done this before, I mean been in this situation before. If I were to give up my baby for adoption, would I have any say on where the baby went to? I mean I don't want the baby to end up in a children's home."

"Most children that are adopted, go to extremely good families, who can provide far more, than a single parent can, in your case, I take it, in an unmarried situation. Families adopt because they can't have their own children and so the adopted child is a very wanted child. We do extensively screen the families that want to adopt and Social Services are required to be involved in the first six months or so. I'm not saying your child couldn't end up in a children's home or with foster carers, but we do everything we can to place the child with the appropriate family." She said tapping her fingers on the desk.

"Will I have to get the Father's permission to put my baby up for adoption?"

"We recommend that you should get permission, before a Court Order is made."

"Will I be able to stay in contact?"

"No absolutely not. We need the child to bond with their adoptive parents. Has anyone discussed the process of adoption with you?"

"No."

"First of all, when you are admitted to hospital, you will be required to inform the nurses, that you are giving up your baby for adoption. The moment your baby is born, it will be taken to a Safe House for six weeks, before being placed for adoption. In your case the baby would be put in the safe custody of a Mrs Bangerter. Social Services will then identify a suitable family for adoption. It will be down to the family, whether or not they want to meet you or not. Most families don't. You will then receive notification in due course, of an application for an adoption order. You may have the right to claim your baby back, but only in extremely rare circumstances, and I have to warn you that would probably not be in the best interests of the child, the child having now bonded with its' adoptive parents."

It took Miriam a while to absorb this information. Her palms were beginning to sweat and she started to rub her tummy.

"I assure you, you would be doing what is in the best interests of the child, in your situation. I am sure you do not need me to make you aware of the alternatives. In the likely event that your child should wish to contact you, they can do so, when they are 18. They will have your name on the birth certificate."

The lady then handed her some leaflets and wrote down some telephone numbers for Miriam. She put them with the other leaflets in her bag and stood up.

"Perhaps you should take some time to think about it and then go and see Mrs Bangerter. Her address is on the back."

When Miriam had said her goodbyes, she went down the stairs, her head heavy with the knowledge she had imparted to her. If only Len wanted this baby, if only he was there to support her, as Patrick had done with her sister? Something was growing inside her, a symbol of the love they had, had for each other. Surely if she had this baby, he would change his mind? She didn't have to make the decision to adopt, until she got to the hospital. Maybe if he realized her intention to go through with the birth he would come round?

That evening she discussed the days' events with her sister. She couldn't go through with an abortion, yet she couldn't go through with an adoption either. She didn't look pregnant but she was starting to feel pregnant. She begged her sister to tell her, what her pregnancy had been like and more importantly what the birth was like? She gave her some information but said Miriam wasn't ready for all the details just yet. She couldn't make a decision based on her experiences, not just yet.

MARJORIE 1967
LONDON

MARJORIE WAS ABSOLUTELY desperate to have the only thing they couldn't have, a baby. They continued with their quest and went to see Mrs Barnet, the senior child care officer at the local family advice centre. She said some people advertised babies in Newsagent windows, which of course she condemned, but it stuck in Marjorie's mind. One day in April 1967, she was chewing over the hopelessness of their attempts so far and suddenly decided that this was the only course left. Orthodox methods were fruitless.

She didn't know where to go, but for some reason, decided on Muswell Hill. She drove there and stopped near the first newsagents, she came to. It was called Cummins and there were a lot of advertisements in the window. She scanned them and there were some, for daily child minders, but nothing more. So she went inside. There was an oldish sensible looking woman in the shop serving some customers.

Marjorie waited until the shop was empty and then approached the counter. The woman was replenishing the cigarette shelves with some Benson and Hedges. The woman would probably think she was some pervert, Marjorie thought, but she had to ask.

"Excuse me? Do you get any advertisements asking for people to look after a baby permanently?"

"I'm sorry, I really don't read the advertisements much. I think it is unlikely."

She paused, whilst rearranging the day's papers. Her eyes were scanning Marjorie, trying to read her intentions. She was so desperate for any information the lady could give her. She really had run out of options.

"Is that what you are hoping to do?" She asked.

"Yes, my husband and I are both over forty and we have been turned down by the Adoption Agency, even as long term foster carers by the children's officer."

"Oh, I'm sorry."

"Oh don't be. It's just we're running out of alternatives. For some reason I had it in my mind that some mothers would want to put up their child for a private adoption."

The woman hesitated and then beckoned her to the back of the shop and started to speak to her in a whisper. There was still no one else in the store.

"Listen, I don't know your circumstances, but you look a nice enough lady. I know someone who looks after babies, for the first six weeks after leaving hospital before they go to the Adoption Society. It's a long shot, but as fortune would have it my son is marrying this woman's daughter soon."

"Oh my goodness, you don't know how grateful I am." Marjorie exclaimed.

She scribbled down on a piece of paper the address "Mrs Bangerter, 41 Ridgeway Avenue, Barnet" and handed it to Marjorie.

"Tell her that Mrs Bouchard, that's me, recommended you go and see her."

"Thank you so much. I don't know how much I can thank you." Marjorie said.

"I wouldn't get your hopes up too soon."

As Marjorie exited the shop she looked up to the skies. There was a God out there she thought, who was finally answering her prayers.

She talked to Arthur about it that evening and they decided to try it. She rang Mrs Bangerter and arranged to go and see her. She explained the whole rigmarole to her, and she said her daughter was getting married in a few weeks and she wasn't looking after any more babies, until that was over. Arthur and Marjorie were going to Austria on 18th June for two weeks, so she was to ring her when they got back. They kept in touch.

MIRIAM 1967
LONDON

OVER THE FOLLOWING months, Miriam decided to distract herself by getting a job in Harrods. The pay was lousy and the hours were long, but it meant that she could pay her way. Every morning she would catch the crowded commuter underground from Muswell Hill to Knightsbridge, changing at King's Cross on to the Piccadilly Line. She had a job working in the ladies department, which meant being on her feet most of the day. At night time she was exhausted. Her sister would always cook her something to eat, when she got back to the flat. Charlotte was nearly eight months now and Miriam got to fuss over and play with her.

"Have you decided what you are going to do sis?"

"I don't know. Part of me thinks Len will come round. I can't go through an abortion now I've seen Charlotte grow."

"You need to talk to Len, or get David to. It's his child as well. His daughters are going to want to know if they have a sibling. Secrets are terrible things sis."

She did phone Len a couple of times. Often, he was too busy to take her calls, busy on some new development project. Her tummy was beginning to show now and she was having difficulty at work in disguising it. She would often wear jackets that were nipped under her chest, so that you couldn't see the rounded form underneath. She tried not to eat for two, so that she could delay handing in her notice at Harrods for as long as possible. Every now and then she would feel the baby move inside her. She felt at times hugely maternal and at other times a huge need to detach herself from this baby. She could not afford to have feelings, less she should have to give this baby away.

Keeping her pregnancy secret from her parents was the hardest thing of all. They wanted to make a trip to come over and see their new grand daughter Charlotte. Under no circumstances could they find out about her pregnancy. Their loyalty to Catholicism forbade it. In the end Orla, made a trip to Ireland to see them, which they thought was slightly odd.

"If you see Len, can you talk to him? I can't bear to phone him again."

"I'll do my best."

When Orla got back from Ireland Miriam was six months pregnant. Patrick was down the local pub, having his constitutional pint of Guinness. Orla and Miriam were sat out on the balcony at the back with Charlotte in the push chair playing with the rattle.

"She has got your eyes you know."

"And Patrick's hair."

"Did you see Len?" Miriam asked. Her sister paused whilst gently rocking the push chair back and forth.

"He's not seeing anyone else, you know. I think he feels that you trapped him. I told him that wasn't the case, that I thought you still had feelings for him. He says, he still has feelings for you, but he already has two children and he doesn't want any more. I think he thinks it will get in the way of his businesses."

Miriam suddenly felt very alone. None of this was meant to have happened. She had, had ambitions of her own, to become a fashion designer. Where had it all gone so wrong? It was time to see Mrs Bangerter. She reached in to her bag and took out the number the lady at the Adoption agency had given to her. She made an appointment to meet her at the house, the following Wednesday. She was only a few streets way.

That day, when she went round to her house, she was shown in to the living room with about six cots lined up in it, most of the babies asleep. There was one baby who was crying and a young girl picked up the baby and began to feed her. They all looked so peaceful in that room.

"I normally look after babies after they have been delivered, for the first six weeks, before they are placed with their adoptive families. It's a tiring job, but very rewarding."

"Do you ever get people asking for private adoptions?" Miriam asked. She had heard that some people arranged private adoptions so they could meet the adoptive parents and so give up their babies for adoption safe in the knowledge that their babies had gone to a good home and not a Children's Home.

"We do get some enquiries. This practice is not strictly legal mind, but come to think of it I did meet a lady recently who is desperate for a child. I think the adoption agency wouldn't let her adopt, because she is a little over the age limit to adopt, which seemed a little harsh. I'll make some further enquiries if you want me to?"

"Yes do." Her own mother had been in her forties when she had Miriam and she didn't see a problem with that.

"Do I have to make a decision now?"

"You'll need to let the Hospital know when you start the contractions, let them get in contact with me."

"Thanks."

On the 4th September 1967, Miriam was tidying around the house as usual, when her contractions started. They kept coming every ten minutes in huge waves. She was feeling nauseous. Her sister had gone out with Charlotte for a walk in the park. She was terrified. No one had prepared her for this amount of pain. She grabbed a coat and hung it on the banisters as the next contraction came. She needed to get to the hospital, but had to wait for this contraction to pass, before she could get down the stairs. Where was her sister when she needed her?

As Miriam stumbled out on to the street, she had to crouch down again on the pavement as the next contraction came.

"Are you alright luv? You look in pain."

"I think I'm in labour."

"Just hold it right there, I'll get a taxi."

With that the man ran off and hailed a cab. He bundled Miriam into the taxi and told him to take her to St Mary's in Paddington, that he was to drive carefully as it would appear that she was in the throws of childbirth. She clung on to the handle bar in the taxi and let out a small scream every time there was a contraction. This baby wanted out in a real hurry. She didn't know if she was going to make it to the hospital. Her sister never told her the pain was going to be this bad.

"Can you hurry please, I don't know if I can take it much longer!"

"I'm driving as fast as I can."

The taxi careered through the streets of London, until it reached Paddington. He drove Miriam up to the entrance of St Mary's hospital and two nurses placed her in a wheelchair and wheeled her into the maternity ward.

"Have your waters broken yet?"

"I don't know."

"That's good then. It sounds as if we have a little time. We may have to break your waters for you. How often are the contractions?"

"About every five minutes I think. Listen." She gasped. "You need to contact a Mrs Bangerter. I am putting the baby up for adoption." She shouted. She didn't know where she found the energy to blurt this out, but Len wasn't here to hold her hand. She couldn't keep this child without him.

Miriam was wheeled into a private room and told to make herself comfortable on the hospital bed. The nurse had a radio on in the room with some classical music on.

"We tend to leave the radio on during the birth to make you more comfortable."

"I can't get comfortable, I'm in agony!"

"Just breath slowly, pant when I say so and push when you feel the baby pushing on your abdomen."

She handed Miriam a mask attached to a machine.

"This will make you woozy. It's gas and air."

She breathed in its' sickly contents. The nurse then broke her waters and she screamed in agony. The pain was getting worse and worse, like an avalanche descending on every part of her body. She breathed in heavily some more gas. She started to go in and out of consciousness and could hear the nurse saying she could see the baby's head.

"Just keep pushing."

She pushed and pushed with every muscle of her body. The nurse was now mopping her brow.

"Not long now Miriam."

With every next push it was like a limb being torn away from her. And then that last push and the sound of a tiny baby crying. She wept and wept from the sheer exhaustion of it all. She had brought a new life into the world, a healthy baby girl, a baby that had been inside her for eight and a half months and was now in the real world.

"Can I hold her?"

"Best not to as she is going up for adoption. We wouldn't want the baby to bond."

"But I want to hold her. Please let me hold my baby girl!" She wailed.

"Now that's quite enough of that nonsense young lady. You shouldn't have got into this mess in the first place. She's better off going to a proper family."

And with that her baby girl was wheeled away in her cot. Miriam never got to touch her or to hold her. It was as if she had given birth and she had died. Tears were streaming down her face. The nurses gave her an injection to induce the afterbirth. This was like giving birth again except this time there was no baby crying at the joy of coming into the world. This was clinical, barbaric even, her body finally exhuming all remnants of her pregnancy. The nurses gave her a sedative and then wheeled her to the maternity ward. There were what seemed like rows and rows of beds with mums and their new born babies, some safely in their cots and sleeping, others fractious for milk. Many had their husbands cooing beside them. She had nothing but an empty cot and no man to comfort her. She wondered where her baby girl was sleeping? Was she with the nurses now or had Mrs Bangerter been in already to collect her, like some package? She stared at the entrance to the ward, willing Len to walk through those doors, but he never came. Slowly the sedative began to take effect and she drifted off to sleep.

"I hope your heart will find the way my darling, darling Michelle".

MARJORIE 1967
LONDON

O N THE 12TH September Marjorie rang Mrs Bangerter.
"Oh I'm so glad you called. We just received a new
addition last week, a delightful baby girl."

"When can I come and see her?"

"This afternoon if you like."

Marjorie put the phone down and ran into the living room. Arthur
was sat in his favourite arm chair reading the Telegraph. Seeing her
excitement he put the paper to one side and removed his glasses.

"You won't believe it." She exclaimed excitedly. " I've just received
a phone call from Mrs Bangerter. She's just received a newborn
baby girl and she said we could go and see her this afternoon!"

"Oh darling I'm so pleased. But don't you think though, we
should tell the children's officer Mrs Barnet. This is the first positive
lead we have had?"

"I think that will ruin our chances. With any luck we might be
able to agree a private adoption with the mother. Then we won't
need the authorities involved."

The last thing Marjorie wanted to do was involve Mrs Barnet. So
far she hadn't come up with any solutions for them as far as

Marjorie could see. If they got her involved she would start questioning their parenting skills and although Arthur had experience of babies, Marjorie had virtually no experience. It couldn't be that difficult though she thought, I mean loads of women had children and mucked along.

That afternoon they jumped into the car and drove straight round to Ridgeway Avenue. On their arrival, Mrs Bangerter led them into the sitting room where there were a row of cots with tiny babies in them. The room smelt of sweet talcum powder. Mrs Bangerter led Marjorie to the cot at the end. There she was, the most beautiful baby girl, eight days old, very small with black hair. Her eyes were closed with her tiny arms splayed either side.

"I've spoken to the mother," she said in a whisper to Arthur and Marjorie. "I've told her about you both and that you are interested in adopting her. She knows that you have been rejected because of your ages, but I don't think she has a problem with that. To be honest, her emotions are all over the place at the moment. She is thinking of going to Ireland for a few weeks to mull things over."

Marjorie was over the moon that they might have found their baby. Arthur and her decided to go and see her mum in Margate and whilst there, they went to see a solicitor and told him about the possibility of having a baby. He advised them to get a letter from the mother saying something to the effect that she was glad they would look after the baby for her, otherwise they might be accused of kidnapping. He also advised them to re write their Wills.

On Tuesday 17th October, the day after they returned from Margate, They went to see Mrs Bangerter again. She had heard nothing from the mother. Marjorie was desperate to know whether she would agree to them having the baby. If she didn't agree, then they might not get another chance.

"If only I knew where she was, I'd go and see her myself." Marjorie blurted out.

"I seem to remember that I scribbled her sister's address somewhere. I don't see any harm in going to see her. I will have to release these babies soon to the Adoption Agency."

She rummaged through some papers in the drawer in the kitchen. After what seemed like an eternity she came back with a brown envelope with the address on it, 14 Danvers Road. Now all Marjorie had to do was meet the mother.

MIRIAM 1967
LONDON

MIRIAM'S SISTER CAME to collect her the next day after she had given birth and over the following days, she just wept and wept, aching for the love of her baby. No one had prepared her for the trauma of giving up her child. She was told she could remain in contact with Mrs Bangerter, but under no circumstances was she to go and see the baby, that she was doing the right thing by her, by putting her up for adoption. A week later, she received a phone call from Mrs Bangerter to say that she had been approached by the woman, again, they had talked about, and was she still interested in a private adoption? She said they were a happily married couple who had been trying for a baby for some time and that they were desperate to adopt a baby. If Miriam went for a private adoption, then she would have the opportunity of meeting the adoptive parents, something that would not happen under the normal adoptive process. Miriam said she would think about it as her emotions were all over the place.

About a month later, just before the six week period was up for Michelle to be placed up for official adoption, Miriam and her sister were sitting in their flat at Danver's Road, when they heard a knock on the door.

"Who's that? Are you expecting anyone sis?" Miriam said

"You stay there. I'll go and get it. I don't want anyone seeing you in this sort of state."

Her sister ran down the stairs and opened the door. She could hear an exchange of voices, with a lady, and came to the door.

"Hi I'm Marjorie."

"You're the lady that wants to adopt Michelle?"

"Yes."

"You'd better come in."

They sat down and chatted for a while. She seemed a nice enough lady, desperate for a child. Miriam confirmed no one knew about this baby in the family except her sister and that it should stay that way. She told her that she was hoping that the father would acknowledge Michelle, but he had not come forward.

"We've been trying so long to have a baby, to make our lives complete. You can be assured we will love her as our own." She said pulling at the hem of her dress. Miriam stared at her sister who was shrugging her shoulders as if to say, what other option do you have? Miriam so needed to get away from the situation that was enveloping her. She had begun to set her mind on taking up a situation as an air stewardess or a cruise stewardess, anything to take her away from the unglamorous situation she had got herself into.

"Do you work Marjorie?"

"No."

"That's good, I don't approve of working mothers. My sister knows I don't approve of her working, but that is her decision."

"My husband has a good job in the City, I can't ever see the need for me to work."

"We thought about my sister looking after Michelle, but Social Services advised against it. In any event my family are fiercely Catholic. They won't accept the baby, unless I marry the father. Can I offer you a drink or anything?"

"No thank you."

She asked Miriam to describe what the father was like and she told her. She also told her a bit about her own family. Marjorie said it would help to have this information to impart to Miriam's baby if she agreed to Marjorie looking after her. She asked if Miriam would mind changing Michelle's name to Rosie as her husband liked that name.

Miriam said she would be happy to sign the papers and for her to change her daughter's name to Rosalie. The whole conversation was entirely surreal, but she had no other option. She had decided to travel to take her mind off things and come to terms with her loss, of her baby and Len. If she didn't agree now, then her baby would be offered up for adoption to a person she had never met. This lady seemed kind, well educated and financially capable of looking after her baby. Most importantly she did not have to go back to work, preferring to remain a housewife.

"If anything should happen to Michelle, I mean Rosie, you will try and let me know? I mean I don't want her to end up in a Children's Home. Any letter sent to Cork with my surname will eventually reach me as we are the only family with that name. However I must stress again, that my Family don't know about this."

"Of course." She replied. They sat in silence for a few moments, the three of them in the sitting room, discussing the future of Miriam's baby that she hadn't even had a chance to hold. It was as if she didn't exist, but she was still every part of her soul. Yet whilst her soul was willing her to keep her, her body was not able to cope.

"There is just one thing." She said. "My lawyers have asked me if you could give me a letter, to say that you agree to me looking after Rosie. I am sorry to trouble you, but would that be possible?"

"I'll do it now."

And with that Miriam got up from the sofa and walked to the small writer's desk in the corner. She picked up a fountain pen and a piece of paper and faced the wall, so Marjorie couldn't see the tears streaming down her face as she wrote the letter.:-

14 Danvers Rd
London N8
18th October 1967

Dear Mrs Ronson

I am very glad you are able to look after my daughter and feel sure she will be very happy with you.

Yours sincerely
Miriam Sullivan-Cody

The lady thanked Miriam and then got up to leave.

"Just a moment." Miriam said "I've got something to give you." It was a spider plant that she had been given at the hospital. It symbolized a connection to her baby. "Please take it?" The woman hesitated. Miriam understood that Marjorie wanted there to be a limited connection between them. Perhaps this threat of her gift frightened her?

"Please take it. It would mean so much if I knew you were watering and nurturing it for me like you are Rosie."

The lady took it and then climbed down the stairs and left the apartment.

"What are you going to do now sis?"

"I honestly don't know. All I know is that I have to get away from here. I've still got some cash left over that Len gave me. May be I'll work on a cruise liner in the Mediterranean, or something."

That night Miriam fell asleep with a heavy heart. It was like some huge bereavement weighing on her shoulders. She realized that the adoption would have to be formalized at some stage. She supposed she didn't want to confront the issue, which felt like some dirty secret. All she had done was agree to let someone else look after her baby for the time being. She prayed hard that night for the safe keeping of her baby.

MARJORIE 1967
LONDON

AFTER LEAVING MIRIAM'S at Danver's Road, armed with a spider plant, Marjorie raced back round to Mrs Bangerter's. She was so elated, she hadn't even found the time to tell Arthur.

"She's agreed to me having Rosie!" She exclaimed to Mrs Bangerter. The woman led Marjorie into the kitchen, and sat her down on the chair next to the window overlooking the garden. She could see the leaves on the trees turning to an autumnal shade of yellow, the October sunshine picking out their slightly burnt hue.

"That sounds brilliant news." She said "But have you got anything in writing?"

"Yes, yes I've got it here."

She reached in to her bag and slowly pulled out the letter and began to unfold it. It wasn't much, but it was all the lawyer had asked for. Mrs Bangerter took out some reading glasses from their case on the kitchen table, with a click and briefly scanned over the document.

"You know this is all highly irregular Marjorie, but I do want to help. I should really tell Social Services you know."

"Oh please don't, they will be all over us like a rash, but I do want to adopt her you know legally, just as soon as the lawyer can get the paperwork together."

"Just be careful, because at your age, they only give foster rights to you. My experience is, the longer you leave it the better."

Marjorie's heart was still racing. When she had gone round to the mother, that afternoon, she hadn't expected her to be so compliant. It was as if she wanted the whole episode to be kept secret as well. She had said time and time again, that she didn't want her parents to find out. Now Marjorie desperately didn't want the authorities to get involved.

"I'll tell you what I can do. I can ring moral welfare officer and tell her that the mother has decided to keep the baby and that there is no need for her to be put up for adoption."

"But the mother has agreed."

"Yes, I know Marjorie, but by doing this, I can keep social services off your back. You can apply for a full adoption order in the fullness of time. You might decide, you don't need to adopt her. The authorities don't always know what is in the best interests of the child."

"That's what I am worried about, that if I don't adopt her, she might decide she doesn't want to be adopted."

"I am sure that won't happen."

"Can I see her?"

"Of course, I'll take you through and make that phone call shall I?"

"Thanks."

She led Marjorie into the sitting room where all the cots were. Rosie was in the cot furthest away from the door. She was wrapped up in her little hospital blanket sleeping. Marjorie gently stroked her forehead. She was still so tiny, it looked as if her limbs might break. Mrs Bangerter had told her that she had been slightly premature, but because she had taken to her bottle, was putting on weight nicely.

"That's it." She whispered. "I've made the phone call. Why don't you come back tomorrow and I'll show you how to bath her, and how to put her nappy and so on. Oh dear, wait a minute, I have to go to a funeral tomorrow."

"Oh don't worry I can babysit, if you like." Marjorie offered "Give me a chance to get to know Rosie."

"Great, that's sorted. I'll see you around 11 o'clock tomorrow."

Marjorie said her goodbyes and jumped into the car back to Barnet. It was now nearly 7 o'clock and Arthur was due at the train station. She decided to go and pick him up and tell him the good news about Rosie. She stood on the platform waiting for the train to draw into the station. As all the commuters piled out of the train she could see his distinct overcoat in the distance. She ran towards him and put her arms around him much to the consternation of the ongoing travellers.

"You'll never believe it! Miriam has agreed."

"What to us having the baby?"

"Yes! And we get to call her Rosie."

"When do we get to see her?"

"Soon, I think. There is so much we need to think of."

The following morning, Marjorie went round to babysit. Mrs Bangerter showed her how to bath Rosie and feed her and then left for the funeral. Her daughter stayed behind to look after the other children. Marjorie picked Rosie up and cradling her in her arms walked towards the kitchen. She had already warmed a bottle of milk in case she cried. Sure enough she started howling straight away, and wouldn't take to her bottle at all. Oh no, Marjorie thought, I'm not a natural at this whatsoever. Maybe this was why I couldn't have children. She tried putting her back down in her cot, but she still carried on screaming. By the time Mrs Bangerter came back Marjorie was panicking.

"I don't know what I am doing wrong. She won't settle at all."

"Don't worry Marjorie, she has somewhat been passed from pillar to post recently. I am sure in the fullness of time she will settle with you."

On the Thursday evening Arthur took Marjorie to the house, so that he could see her. She was fractious at being got up at an unaccustomed time and he took to her, Marjorie thought more than he would have done had she been placid.

"You obviously have a way with babies, Mr Ronson." Said Mrs Bangerter.

Part of Marjorie was a little upset that it seemed to be easier for him to bond with the baby than herself. She knew it made sense because Arthur had had babies before, she just hoped that by being a woman, her maternal instinct would have clicked in. Perhaps she hadn't appreciated how challenging looking after a baby was going to be.

On Saturday 21st October, Arthur and Marjorie decided to go shopping to Mothercare for a carry-cot, transporter, blankets, nappies, and also to other places for bottles, teats, vests, nighties, booties, pants, sheets, cotton shawls, towels, SMA, farex and robinson foods. They also each got her a little toy.

"I can't believe how much we had to buy!" Marjorie said as they were carrying the shopping back to the car. "It must have cost a small fortune."

"It's better, in my experience to be over prepared. There won't be much time for shopping when we have her at home."

At six o'clock, they went over to Mrs Bangerter to collect her. She had two grandchildren there, with her, Melanie aged nine and a boy a bit older. Melanie was very interested in Rosie, but not the boy and Mrs Bangerter was so busy snapping at him to say "Good Evening" to them, she forgot to introduce Arthur and her husband. They grinned at each other and Arthur said.

"We don't get a look in when there are babies around."

Marjorie hoped that Arthur didn't think that having Rosie would alter the way they felt about each other. To the contrary she saw having this little baby in their lives, making their love for each other stronger. She knew his first wife had not been a good wife or a good mother. She was determined to show Arthur, she could be both.

That evening, they took Rosie home and gave her an SMA feed straight away. She gazed around the living room while taking it in, obviously aware she was in a fresh place. Eventually Marjorie put her down in her cot, but she cried and cried. Arthur said they should wait awhile and see if she settled down, but she didn't.

"Oh Arthur, what are we doing wrong?"

"Nothing, she just needs nursing for awhile."

With that, he got up and picked her up and nursed her in his arms until she finally fell asleep. She looked so vulnerable in his big, strong arms. It was hard to think that this tiny human being would one day grow into an adult. All she needed now was love and nurturing.

The following morning, while Marjorie was cooking lunch, Arthur carried her round the house showing her things. She heard him say.

"This is a mirror, you can see yourself in it, look."

He then drew a face on the window for her. Then he went out in to the garden and picked some late autumn flowers for her to smell. He showed her gradually every sight and sound he could give her.

Over the next few weeks, Marjorie lived in fear of the Children's Welfare Officer, Mrs Barnet coming over, or hearing about her, or meeting her with her. She remembered the first time she went out shopping with her. She was absolutely tense, but people in shops so often admired her. She felt relieved. She decided the best thing was to say to herself.

"OK, they may come and take her away tomorrow, so let this be a happy day"

The only person she told was her next door neighbour who was over the moon for them.

"If anyone asks about Rosie, can you just say we are looking after her for somebody?"

"Of course Marjorie. I know how much you wanted this child."

"I'm just so afraid the authorities will come after us."

"Listen, it is not as if you've kidnapped her or something. The mother agreed didn't she?"

"Yes I know, but I read somewhere that you are duty bound to tell the local authority at some stage. I just think the longer we have

Rosie and the longer we have to bond, the harder it will be for the authorities to intervene."

"Your secret is safe with me Marjorie."

Their kind neighbours lent them a cot which they used at night. Arthur loved her and often fed her and sat with her watching television on his knee. He wheeled her in to the dining room, while Marjorie was putting supper on the table, and sat her up in the corner of the carry cot, supported against a blanket. She would often solemnly watch them eating, like a little mandarin.

They had Rosie in the room with them during the evening, as she slept a lot during the day and she lay in her carry cot, bicycling or sat on a knee watching television, or mountaineering, or climbing up one of them, particularly when Arthur was wearing his navy pullover. Towards Christmas, Marjorie was afraid Miriam might get in touch, but she did not. Her mother came to them for Christmas, and was delighted with Rosie. Arthur and Marjorie gave Rosie a penguin suit for Christmas, among other things and they had a happy Christmas.

Then on Monday 15th January 1968, eight weeks after they had taken possession of Rosie, Marjorie received a phone call.

"Marjorie Ronson?"

"Yes speaking."

"This is Doctor Rosenberg, from St Bart's Hospital."

Her heart was pounding in her chest. What could possibly have happened? Was it her mother, was it Arthur, had they called to take away her daughter?

"It's your husband. He suffered a massive heart attack at work this morning. We have managed to stabilize him, but I suggest you come to the hospital right away."

"But he's only fifty four."

"I know, these things hit us when we least expect it. Is there a history of heart disease within the family Mrs Ronson?"

"No! I mean I don't know."

Marjorie was rattling her brains. Come to think about it Arthur had mentioned that his brother, who was a surgeon, was very careful with his diet. She hadn't thought to ask Arthur what that was all about. He smoked occasionally, but who didn't after the War.

"Is it serious?"

"As I say we have stabilized him at the moment but he may drift in and out of consciousness and possibly go into a coma."

"I'll be there just as soon as I can doctor."

She slammed the phone down and ran into her next door neighbour's. Rosie was fast asleep in her cot thank goodness.

"Jacqueline!"

"Marjorie, whatever is the matter?"

"It's Arthur! He has been rushed in to St Bart's with a massive heart attack. Can you take care of Rosie for me?"

"Of course."

"All her bottles and SMA are in the kitchen, her nappies are in the bathroom," she blurted out in a panic.

"Just go, Marjorie, I'll be fine. I've been there before remember!"

And with that she dashed out of the house and caught the first train to London. At Kings Cross, she changed to get on to the Circle line. As the train stopped at each station, she was willing the train to go faster and faster. Not now please Oh Lord, I've only just gained Rosie, don't whatever you do lose me Arthur.

As Marjorie got to Farringdon, she ran out of the station until she got to the entrance of St Bart's. The hospital was huge and she scanned corridor after corridor until finally arriving at Accident and Emergency.

"I'm looking for my husband Mr Ronson."

"He has been transferred to Intensive care, I'm afraid."

Oh Lord, please let her get there on time. She eventually found him in a private room off Ward B. He was strapped up to all sorts of machines and monitors. There were two male nurses standing by the bed taking notes.

"Are you his wife?" one of them asked.

"Yes."

"I'm afraid he is heavily sedated you know."

She stared at the bed. Arthur's face was sheet white with his eyes closed. His hand had an intravenous drip inserted. Attached to his chest were various electrodes which in turn were attached to another monitor which constantly went beep. She sat down in the chair beside him and idly stroked his forehead.

"Don't leave me now Arthur, I can't do this on my own."

His eyes flickered slightly as if registering her presence. She could see that his heart was still beating. His flesh was still warm and she clung on to his hand willing for a response. She carried on sitting there for the next hour or so watching him sleeping. Eventually a monitor sounded an alarm and a doctor appeared.

"It is alright Mrs Ronson. That alarm is just to warn us that he is coming round and may need some more sedative."

"Can I just talk to him? For a few moments?"

"Yes, but try to keep it brief. He is very weak."

She turned towards Arthur, trying to hold back the tears, so he couldn't see how upset she was.

"Arthur, can you hear me?"

His eyes started to open and his head slowly rolled to the left to look at her.

"I've written a will and Rosie's in it," he whispered.

"Don't talk about wills at a time like this. You' re going to get better."

"I'm tired, very very tired."

"Love you."

The doctor came back and gave him a sedative. Marjorie watched Arthur as he closed his eyes and fell back to sleep.

"Best come back in the morning after you have had a good night's sleep Mrs Ronson. There's nothing more you can do here until the morning."

She knew she had to get back for Rosie. She couldn't expect Jacqueline to look after her through the night as well. With a heavy heart, she left his bedside, and took the train back to Barnet.

"What's the prognosis?" said her neighbour over a strong shot of brandy.

"I don't know."

That night she slept fretfully. Thankfully Rosie was sleeping through the night now, otherwise, she didn't know how she would have coped.

The following morning she rose early in a panic. She simply had to get back to the hospital. She couldn't leave Arthur on his own, but she couldn't leave Rosie alone either. Jacqueline had promised to look after her the previous night for as long as she needed her.

Marjorie didn't have any other option at the moment. She would have to get Jacqueline to call her mum and get her to come up to London.

"Marjorie, don't fret, just get yourself to the hospital. I've managed twins you know."

She was grateful to the one friend and neighbour she had got in Jacqueline. Nothing had prepared her for this. She hurriedly took the train that morning and dashed back to the hospital. When she arrived at the Arthur's bedside she noticed that he was still sleeping. After updating herself as to his progress during the night which was pretty much the same as the day before she went down to the canteen to get a strong cup of black coffee and some flowers to place by Arthur's bedside. When she returned his eyes were open, but he was still very sleepy.

"Arthur," she said squeezing his hand." You gave us quite a fright yesterday."

Arthur blinked acknowledging his response and then gazed at the flowers.

"I brought you some daffodils and tulips, a message that spring has sprung. I'll just put them in some water for you."

She grabbed an empty vase from the window sill and went to the bathroom to fill it with water.

"There we are." She said on her return "I never liked hospitals."

At that moment the doctor walked in with two of his assistants. He checked the handwritten chart at the bed and then checked Arthur's pulse.

"Morning Mrs Ronson."

"Morning Doctor?"

"Doctor Mamford. Listen Mrs Ronson, I know you must be in shock right now after yesterday's attack. We have managed to stabilize your husband and as you can see he is awake, but I would suggest that you give him as much rest as possible at the moment. I know the temptation must be to talk to him but I would advise against this until he has regained some strength. We will keep him on the drip for the time being and keep you updated as to his progress."

"You will let me know if there is any change doctor? You see I have a young baby to look after and I don't like to leave her for long periods at a time."

"Of course, Mrs Ronson."

She kissed him softly on the head and then picked up her things and left. The sun was beating down outside but this did nothing to lighten her mood. How was she going to cope? Surely Arthur would get through this? Why now when they had just got Rosie? On the way to the tube station she popped into a church which was full of homeless people. She tried to feel sorry for their predicament, but couldn't. She knelt down and said a little prayer and then lit a candle for Arthur.

When she got home that evening she didn't feel like eating anything. She went to collect Rosie and placed her in the playpen whilst she made the phone call to her mother.

"I am so sorry darling, Jacqueline told me."

"I feel so helpless mum. They have told me that he must get as much rest as possible, but all I want to do is talk to him, to reassure myself he is still with us. He's so young."

Marjorie knew that his job was stressful but had no idea what had brought this on.

"Perhaps when he shows signs of getting better, which he will love, we should take Rosie in to see him. She will make him smile."

"I know, but hospitals are such awful places."

They did take Rosie to see Arthur the following week, when he showed signs of getting better. Arthur was sat up in his hospital bed supported by his pillows. He was no longer on a drip but was still attached to a heart monitor which constantly went beep. Rosie slept most of the time in her travel cot but at least Arthur got to see her.

Marjorie continued to see him on a daily basis whilst her mother looked after Rosie.

"Arthur you do know I love you," she said tears streaming down her face.

"You have to be strong for Rosie."

"I can't do this without you, you are my soulmate. Everything else means nothing."

She carried on talking but Arthur wasn't listening as he was drifting in and out of consciousness.

One night, she sat on the Northern line on her way back to Barnet watching the tube signs go by in a blur. She knew something was wrong and couldn't put her finger on it. The monotonous beat of the train numbed her senses.

When she arrived home she received the inevitable phone call.

"Mrs Ronson, I'm sorry to tell you that your husband passed away at 4.40pm this afternoon of two massive heart attacks. I'm afraid there was nothing we could do."

MIRIAM 1968
MEDITERRANEAN

T HAT WINTER MIRIAM applied and got accepted to
work as a stewardess on the Queen Frederica which was
operating cruises in the Mediterranean under charter to Sovereign
Cruises. She flew down to Malta to board the vessel. Queen
Frederica's had just undergone extensive refurbishment and its'
sleek design and air-conditioning, offered supreme comfort. As a
result she was often referred to as the "Millionaire's ship". Her
profile was distinguished by her clipper-like bow, single mast and
impressive funnel as well as her cruiser stern and absence of rigging.

On reaching the gang way, she was greeted with a sign saying
"Welcome Home" at the end of the gang plank. She had only
travelled light as she suspected she would be spending most of her
time in uniform. She was greeted by an officer in whites with his
name badge on, "Officer Briggs". He was handsome in a refined
sort of way. She liked to see men in uniform.

"Morning miss." He said saluting her. "Passenger or crew."

"Crew." Miriam said reluctantly

"Access to the crew deck is at the forward end. Access to the
crew accommodation is down the aft end, on your starboard side."

"I'm sorry, I don't understand."

"You'll soon get the hang of it. Basically turn right and you'll find your accommodation on the other side of the ship."

"Thanks."

She walked the length of the liner, until she reached the starboard side. On either side of the ship there were garden lounges spread along the promenade deck with large framed windows overlooking the sea. Between these lounges, she had read, there was a comfortable theatre, fully equipped for the pleasant presentation of the best in motion pictures, that Hollywood could find. She entered into the main lounge and smoking lounge, which was comfortably appointed for relaxation and conversation. Here the rugs and upholstery were softly hued, the easy chairs large and deep and the walls panelled in warmly toned veneer. From here she ventured into the cocktail lounge. The design was dramatic with its' raised balconies enclosed within balustrades of light silver metal. Then there was the broad bar itself, sweeping the length of the room with an air of sophistication.

Outside in addition to the deck space allotted to the shuffle board and tennis, there was also a huge outdoor swimming pool and a gymnasium.

"It's pretty impressive isn't it?" said a young woman beside her. Miriam guessed from looking at her that she was about the same age as her. Her hair was blonde and neatly cupped her face. Her accent was clipped, the sort of accent you had if you had been to boarding school in England.

"Are you looking for the crew quarters?"

"Yes."

"Then follow me. I'm used to doing the chalet season in the Alps, but my parents thought it a good idea to do some work experience on the cruise ships this year. I think they are secretly hoping to marry me off to some millionaire, if truth be known. I just plan to have a hoot! What's your name?"

"I'm Miriam."

"I'm Lucy. I hope we can become good friends. I get awfully sea sick you know."

"The only time I've been on a boat is when I go back to Ireland."

"I don't think the Med is meant to be as rough as the Irish Sea, but who knows?"

They walked down the ship until they reached some water tight doors with a sign saying "Crew" above it. To the right was the access corridor to the crew pub the "Pig and Whistle". To the left you could feel a continuous blast of hot air from the permanently open door at the top of the companionway down to the engine room. They walked down a corridor marked "Ladies Accommodation" with rooms either side with two beds in.

"I say we bags this one on the left."

They threw their luggage on the beds and sat down opposite each other. There was a little porthole to the right with a window looking out to sea. In the corner was a small wash basin and vanity unit. No one had briefed them as to what the schedule was. There was a letter of welcome which they read on the side.

"Looks as if tonight they just want us to get to know everybody. The real training starts tomorrow. I know some first class passengers are boarding with their own staff, but the majority don't come on board until we set sail for Italy on Friday."

That evening they all congregated in the crew pub and met the other crew. The officers right down to the porters were there all exchanging their experiences. It was a transient crowd of people, some who had met before, others who hadn't. It was like bringing together the cast of a theatre. Probably each of them had their own stories that they were running away from. This transience suited Miriam for now. She had not sorted out any plans for her own future. Her parents knew she was anxious to see a bit more of the world and her father had been very supportive. He was a travel writer and had asked her to promise to give him some reviews of the cruise for his publisher. She couldn't stop thinking about Rosie, the baby she never got to hold. Hopefully this time on the ocean would help her to come to terms with her loss.

Over the following weeks they set sail. The mood was buoyant on that cruise liner. The work was hard, but the passengers were polite and undemanding. They gave them the very best in service. The company motto at the time was.

"A kind of pride typifies a Frederic worker, pride in a job well done, pride and over a century of experience."

Lucy was pretty sea sick on the crossing over to Italy. The seas were rough and even though the ship was large it didn't stop them being tossed and turned on those corridors. Even the waiters had to abandon serving trolleys as the crockery was smashing all over the place. For some reason, maybe it was because she'd experienced pregnancy, she didn't feel so sea sick. She nursed her new friend on that crossing. Some of the other crew members said that it would get better with time when she finally got her sea legs.

"You'd make a good mum you know." She said.

Miriam's heart ached when she said that. Little did she know that she was a mum, albeit a bereaved mum. She wondered how Rosie was doing now with her new mum and dad? She daren't contact her for fear of upsetting their new relationship. She had been told that they had to have time to bond. Any interference with that bonding would damage their relationship. Yet she wanted to bond too. The only way to obliterate her memory was when she was in an Irish drunken stupor at night time. She would always end up crying herself to sleep on those evenings.

There was a lot of flirting going on in the crew pub on those evenings, but Miriam wasn't prepared for a relationship with anyone right now. In any event, to form a relationship on the boat seemed too complicated for her. If you ended up falling out, how could you avoid each other? Lucy formed a relationship with one of the officers, which didn't work out.

"Men, I hate them. He promised me the world, then I wouldn't sleep with him and he dumped me."

"Just as well you didn't." Miriam said.

She couldn't tell her about Rosie. They weren't quite close enough yet and she didn't want someone to tell her how stupid she had been or tell her to contact her. She wanted to so much. Being off shore made it easier not to.

One day Lucy came bursting in to their cabin screaming excitedly.

"You'll never guess who is on board!"

"Who?"

"Freddie Laker. Just embarked at Italy to go to Monaco."

Freddie Laker had just founded Laker Airways. He had been in the news a lot recently and was proposing to offer a brand new revolutionary concept of economic air travel, requiring passengers to purchase their tickets on the day of travel as well as buy their own food. He was divorced and in his forties. Miriam could not work out what Lucy was so excited about apart from the fact that he was a man of power.

"My parents would be so impressed!"

"Lucy, I doubt we'll get to meet the guy. It depends whether we get deployed to first class or not. That depends on Tony."

"Can you ask him Miriam? Please."

That evening in the Pig and Whistle, Miriam asked Tony the Chief Officer if they could be deployed in first class, when they set sail for Monaco.

"That depends if there is something in it for me."

"Don't tease me Tony, I'm not in to men any more."

"I've noticed, more's the pity. He must have been some tough nut to let you go."

"Will you let us go then?"

"Let me see what I can do with the shift schedules. I can probably shift you to the cocktail bar on the top deck for a week."

"Thanks Tony, you're a star."

There was quite a bit of press interest when Freddie Laker disembarked for the day in Naples. There were flash photographers everywhere and a few TV cameras. Airline travel was starting to pick up in a big way and would soon eclipse the cruise liners as the main form of travel. Whilst Miriam wasn't interested in Freddie Laker she was keen to be an air stewardess one day. The job looked glamorous and you got to see the world. Anything to take her mind off losing Rosie. There were a lot of hushed whispers amongst the staff that day.

"Have you seen Freddie Laker. I'm sure he smiled at me." Lucy remarked.

That evening Miriam put on her first class uniform, which was smarter than the crew's. It was a black evening cocktail dress with a black, white and gold scarf tied around her neck and draped down her back. To match, she wore some black stockings and some black patent court shoes. Lucy was donning the same, whilst she applied some black khol eyeliner and some red lipstick.

"Wow ! You look amazing." Lucy cried.

"I've told you Lucy, I'm not into men. I'm doing this for you."

They walked in tandem, past some of the officers, to the sound of wolf whistles. When they entered the cocktail bar, the lights were low. The huge glass windows gave an unparalleled view of the ocean at night. The moon was flickering on the waves of the sea. A pianist was playing soft jazz music in the corner. The chief cocktail waiter was shaking cocktails in his cocktail mixer. The silver bar seemed to reach forever along the starboard side of the liner. The bar was beginning to fill up with the evening diners in their cocktail attire. The chief cocktail waiter showed them the ropes and how to address the guests.

When Freddie Laker did walk into the room later that evening there was a certain hush in the room as he entered. He was with an entourage of men. People were trying to get a glimpse of him whilst pretending not to notice him. He came straight up to the bar and approached Miriam, his eyes engaging her.

"Why do people always pretend they don't know you, when they know exactly who you are? Could I have a gin and tonic please, gentleman what can I get you, the same?"

She grabbed the glasses and with the silver ladles nursed the ice cubes in to the heavy crystal glasses. She splashed them with a few large shots of gin and poured the tonics in allowing them to settle in the glass.

"I'm not pretending." She smiled

"Interesting."

He had quite a presence in that room, his voice bellowing out with laughter. Here was a man that clearly liked to party. Miriam could see that Lucy was disappointed that he hadn't approached her first. He kept looking in Miriam's direction to see if she was eavesdropping the conversation.

"I'm going to take the skies by storm. There will be no more cruise liners in the next decade, you mark my words. Everyone will want to travel by air. We'll make sure we have the prettiest stewardesses like this one." He caught Miriam's eye as he dropped this comment.

"Would you come and work for my airline young lady?"

"That would depend on the terms."

"I can see you're a tough negotiator. When do you get shore leave?"

"Not so fast sir. I haven't said I'm interested."

He picked up the piece of paper on the silver tray and scribbled his number on it.

"Give me a call when we dock in Monaco. I'll show you the sights. Bring a friend if you like."

With that they left to go to dinner. They didn't see him again that evening, but they were to see him every night in the bar before he went to dinner. He was an affable bloke. He certainly knew how to have fun and how to not take life too seriously. That sort of fitted with Miriam's life right now. She couldn't bear the thought of commitment. She couldn't bear to talk about the child she had lost, all those miles away. The sea was her comfort now, ebbing away in the night time.

When they docked at Monaco, they were entitled to shore leave for a couple of days. She decided to call him and he invited her and her friend Lucy to his boat for the day in the harbour. The sun was beating down that day on the little Principality dubbed by Somerset Maugham "A sunny place for shady people". They got very drunk, drinking his champagne and downing a mixture of lobster and caviar. They sunbathed in their bikinis on the decks and after getting rosy from the sun and champagne, hit the night clubs until the early hours.

"That was one of the best days of my life." Said Lucy.

The weeks, turned into months on that cruise ship. Freddie Laker agreed to stay in touch, should they dock again and he could see them on their offshore leave. They had many such get togethers, but they were harmless fun. Miriam thought Lucy would have liked something more with one of his colleagues. She kept in touch by writing long letters. Lucy and Miriam became close friends on that cruise ship. On the 4th September 1968, a year after Rosie was born, she was drinking with Lucy in the crew pub. Everyone was having far too much to drink.

"Don't you ever think of settling down and having children?" Lucy asked.

Her question hit Miriam like a bombshell. Her baby's birthday was today, the day she had given birth. Was she walking now? Was she saying her first words? She so wanted to shower her with kisses, tell her she loved her with all her heart. Tears started to trickle down her face.

"Oh Miriam, I'm sorry. Is it something I said?"

"Do you mind if we go outside for a bit. I need some fresh air and a cigarette?"

"Sure."

They grabbed their coats and hit the night air. The liner was picking up speed now, crashing through the waves. The sky was illuminated by millions of little stars. Miriam stared at those stars for a very long time.

"I often think of her, you know. I often wish on those stars to wonder where she is right now."

"What do you mean Miriam?"

"I have a little baby. She is one today, but I can't be with her because I had to give her away. There is not a day that does not go by, when I can't stop thinking about her."

"Oh Miriam, I'm sorry. What happened to the father?"

"Oh he didn't want to know. I loved him you know. I loved him with all my heart, but he broke it."

"Do you think you will ever love again?"

"No, not in this lifetime."

"Can't you get in contact with her, your baby I mean?"

"They tell you not to. They say it is in the best interests of the child. That doesn't stop me aching for her though. It is like a constant bereavement."

After telling Lucy, coming to terms with Miriam's loss seemed easier somehow. Now she had someone to confide in. Christmas came and went and was just as traumatic for her. Unfortunately she was to receive the tragic news that her brother James had died of a road accident in Ireland. That together with losing Rosie was a double tragedy. Nevertheless they continued to sail the Mediterranean, lapping up the European culture. Over the months they visited Malta, Cyprus, Jerusalem, Turkey, Yugoslavia and Greece. They never tired of these destinations. She never stopped thinking about Rosie though.

MARJORIE 1968
LONDON

NOTHING HAD PREPARED Marjorie for the death of Arthur. For days she stayed locked up in her house trying to make sense of it all. Jacqueline kindly took possession of Rosie, whilst she handled all the necessary funeral arrangements and dealt with the wealth of correspondence that came in from friends and relatives. On the 3rd February she wrote.

"Why do people say that time will heal? I don't want to be healed of the pain of losing my love. No I don't. I want to feel he is still part of my life. I don't just want to feel it, I want it to be so. If real love doesn't die why should this be wrong?

I don't know how long this can go on because conditions change, and new situations arise. Rosie will grow bigger and not remember him. How enormously different people are from one another. I feel as though there is something I should be doing, but don't know what it is? Or as though there is something just round the corner. Life goes steadily on, then suddenly there's an immense surge, like a tidal wave, or a whirlwind, and one is buffeted and tossed and things are never the same again. I'm not sure this particular whirlwind is over yet. It seems more and more to me that the world lacks substance. So much is pretense, false reasons, sham enthusiasms. Only true love is real and when that is snatched away, what is there? Just duty and trivialities and waiting to die.

I can't believe Arthur won't come back, I keep expecting him. When Jacqueline said the other day "Where's Uncle Ronson?" I said "Oh hell he will be coming back soon" and it came out just like that because part of me thinks that he will. I just can't believe we won't hug and cuddle one another again. He's so real to me. But I must believe it. But can't we go on together, even though I'm in this world and he is not? Can't love bridge the gaps? It's something not soluble by thought, thinking distorts it. It is something to be discovered by living it, just as love is.

What I want to know is this. Is this love lost when someone dies, is it just cut off, like a flower is severed for ever from the plant it grew on? Father Ryan said there was no male or female in the after life and of course it says so in the New Testament. I just can't imagine that, it must be awful.

So much joy was denied Arthur, he had such a miserable bleak life most of the time, then just as he'd found such joy in Rosie, he said so often "Darling I'm so happy with you and Rosie" he dies. I used to think that people died from purely physical causes, but I'm not at all sure now. Many people go on with bad hearts for years and years and he'd not had heart trouble before. I think he was taken and I don't know why.

We are surrounded by mysteries. We accumulate a lot of knowledge, but the important things elude us. We don't really know what happens to our loved ones, when they die. We are left with the pain of knowing we will never hear the voice of a loved one again, or be able to touch him or feel his touch. When I die how shall I find him? How will I know him? Worst of all will it matter any more? I love to think he will be waiting for me, like he used to wait at the ticket collector's box at the station, patiently waiting, never cross if I was late, always with a hug and a kiss and we'd drive back here in a bubble.

Why can't we know? Is it so terrible? Or is it so beautiful? Or is it, something which requires faculties which we haven't got in this life? If so are we developing these faculties in this life without knowing it?

The thing that remains with me is the unfairness of it to Arthur. All our married life, I longed for a baby, and he was so patient about it. Then we got Rosalie and he loved her and delighted in her so much. His joy in her was like a wonderful bonus to having her at all. Then when we'd only had her eight weeks, he was taken from us and died. All the love and joy they could have had were cut off forever, and she'll have no memory of him.

And it was so in other ways. All those dreary years after his first marriage broke up. When he was alone, he spent so little on himself, just went quietly on doing the best he could for the boys.

I decanted the wine we made together the other day and it was beautiful, sparkling, clear and strong, but he's not here to enjoy it. He had so little of the wine of life. His sons thanked me for making his last years happy. I suppose I did to some extent, but I was enriched beyond reckoning by his love and I wish I'd been more loving, and on many occasions I can think of, more understanding and kind."

Marjorie couldn't carry on like this she had to get on and live her life for Rosie. Now that she had lost Arthur, she couldn't possibly lose Rosie as well. There was still a real danger that she could be taken away from her too. All she had was Miriam's letter which just confirmed that she was happy for her to look after her. There was nothing in that letter that confirmed she could legally adopt her. Rosie was all she had left.

On 22nd March 1968, two months after Arthur died, she went to see her lawyer about Rosie.

"I must say Mrs Ronson, that these are tragic circumstances indeed. I would think that if the matter were to go to Court today, the real mother would have a strong argument to have her back if she wanted." He said twiddling his fountain pen between his fingers.

"But I can't lose her now, Mr Maitland. Rosie is all I have left! The mother did say I could look after her."

"Mrs Ronson, I need not tell you I'm sure, but applying for an adoption order, is a serious matter. The Court will look at what is in the best interests of the child. In your case you are now a single parent, now aged 45 who I suspect is still trying to cope with some difficulty, the premature death of her husband. The mother in this case Miriam has every right under the Adoption Act 1958 to change her mind until an adoption order is made. I take it you haven't told the mother yet about your latest loss."

"No."

"The Court may indeed take the view that you yourself need bereavement counselling. They may take the view that this is not entirely the most satisfactory environment to bring up a child."

The tears started to stream down her face.

"But what if the mother doesn't want her and then Rosie has to go in to a Children's Home?"

"It is not for me to judge the view the Court would take in such a situation. Suffice it to say from where I am sitting, the odds are not stacked in your favour."

She grabbed some tissues from the tissue box on the table and wiped her nose. She knew Miriam had asked her to let her know if Rosie's circumstances changed. She also knew in her heart of hearts that if she thought there was any danger that Marjorie had to go back to work that she would definitely want her back. She had enough money to tie her over for the time being, but the probate for the will still needed to be sorted out. As if reading her thoughts Mr Maitland said.

"I know we've yet to sort out the details of your husband's estate, but I can let you know that you will be well provided for and that there is a provision in there for Rosie."

""But I need to know that she is mine, that the authorities can't take her away from me."

"Mrs Ronson, if you apply for an Adoption Order now, you will be seriously jeopardizing your position. May I suggest, you see how the land lies over the next six months and then make an appointment to see us again. As I reiterate I am not a family law expert, because as you know I mainly deal in wills and probate, but since you are a former employee, I am happy to advise you in a private capacity. If

I were a family law expert I may well consider that I have a conflict of interest, to do in what the Courts will look at what is in the best interests of the child."

On the 23rd October, Marjorie went to see him again and the lawyer took notes on what had happened. She reiterated that the situation was becoming untenable, as she was having to duck and dive every time she went out somewhere with Rosie. This time he said he would make some tentative enquiries about her chances of adopting her.

Things dragged on for another year until she was finally told that the lawyer had left the firm. By now Rosie was starting to talk and she couldn't bear to live in this state of secrecy any longer. She spoke to the lawyers over the telephone and on her instruction they agreed to put in an application for adoption on 5th March 1969.

On Saturday 8th March 1969, Rosie fell on a plastic spike and got an awful black eye. She was screaming her head off and Marjorie could see blood trickling down her face. Oh my God she thought, what if she has blinded herself in one eye?

"Calm down my love." Marjorie said rocking her until she stopped crying. "The doctor will make it better." She telephoned the doctor, who said it would probably be alright but it would be best to go to casualty to check it out. She was terrified that if she went to casualty, there would be some record of Rosie that Social Services would grab hold of. She didn't know what to do. What was best for Rosie, wasn't necessarily best for Marjorie. She telephoned her mum.

"What am I to do mum?" She said with Rosie screaming in the background.

"You must take her to casualty love. Get the doctor to check her out. At the very least she will need something to cope with the pain by the sound of things."

She grabbed her keys and coat and bundled Rosie in to the mini. The nearest hospital was the County Hospital in Barnet. It took them ten minutes to get there. When she reached casualty, the nurses ushered them into a concealed cubicle and told them to wait for the doctor to arrive. A few minutes later, a nice young Asian man appeared and examined Rosie's eye with a small torch.

"It seems that a bit of the membrane has been torn, but the eye is alright, Mrs Ronson. You were very lucky on this occasion. I will get one of the nurses to wash it and put some antiseptic ointment on it. I'm afraid it won't look very sightly for a while."

"Thanks Doctor. Will she be able to see alright?"

"It will remain swollen for a week or so, but she will be able to see again."

With that the doctor smiled and went to see the next patient. The nurse tended to Rosie's swollen eye, which was now black and blue and swollen. She took her home that evening and gave her, her supper. Marjorie thought the pain must have started subsiding as she ate her food and then went to sleep.

Over the next week, she watched her as the swelling started to subside. Don't worry, she kept telling herself, accidents happen to children all the time. She finally got the all clear at the hospital the following Friday.

Marjorie was on tenterhooks that week in case the children's officer came. She didn't want her to be greeted by Rosie with a black eye. Anyway it had cleared up by the time she made her first visit which was on the 21st March. She was quite pleasant, asked how Rosie had come to have the name Rosalie, so Marjorie told her. There was nothing tricky to answer that time. She asked if she had any problems with Rosie and she said "No."

Their family doctor and friend Doctor Langford called the following Tuesday and thereafter, came once a week, so as to be able to rebut anything damaging the children's officer might say.

"You see Doctor Langford, there is a real chance that the mother could take her away from me. I don't trust social services. You know I will always love her as my own, that I will look after her?

"Marjorie, rest assured, I am doing this as your family friend. I think you make a good mother."

On 30th June Marjorie received a phone call from the children's officer who asked her to go and see her at her office for an interview. The date for the adoption hearing had been fixed for 24th July. Marjorie supposed the children's officer suddenly realized she hadn't done very much. That and the fact that Marjorie had deliberately tried to avoid any contact if it could be helped.

"Marjorie, can I call you that if I may?" She said

"Yes that is OK." She put Rosie down in a small play pen that was provided. Rosie was starting to crawl now and she didn't want any more accidents to happen.

"Have you made any attempt to contact the birth mother?"

"No, I mean I haven't, but my solicitors have, at the Danvers Road address. One got no reply and the other got returned."

"So, have you made any other efforts to find her?"

"No, not particularly."

"Well if not, how did you originally find her?"

Marjorie twisted her hands together and glanced over at Rosie. She couldn't say she'd approached Mrs Bangerter through the back door. Her mind was panicking.

"I met her through a friend of mine, who knew we wanted children." She could see the children's officer holding on to her every word.

"She has since died." She added.

The children's officer raised her eyebrow. She asked if Marjorie had any correspondence about it and she said she had a letter from the mother, saying she was glad she would look after Rosie.

She told Marjorie to bring that letter along and they would take a photocopy of it. She asked when Marjorie had met the mother. Marjorie was beginning to feel quite stressed out at this stage. She said on the Monday or a Tuesday in October 1967 she had called at Danvers Road. They had talked for a bit, and she had told Marjorie she felt she'd rather know the person Rosie was going to, rather than place her with an adoption society and never know who she was sent to. She said she received a letter from her that day and then went to pick Rosie up on the Saturday. She couldn't remember the number of the house, or the name of the woman that put her in touch with her.

"I'm sorry Marjorie, but I don't find this all very satisfactory. Research has shown that it is better to wait until the child is nine or ten years of age before we formalize an adoption. I would say this is particularly so in your case, bearing in mind your recent bereavement. The child can then have a say as to whether or not they want to be adopted."

"I totally disagree."

"Perhaps you are afraid Rosie will choose not to be adopted by you?"

"No, of course not." She paused for thought. She couldn't stop that niggling feeling in the back of her mind that she might make this decision. This is why she simply had to adopt her now.

"I don't care what the common consensus is, I just don't think that, that is the sort of decision a child should have to make."

"Marjorie, you probably have no need to fear that Rosie would not choose to be adopted, or go back to her birth mother, but research has shown that this is a good idea, so that any difficulties or problems can be ironed out then."

All the time her mind was swimming with thoughts of Miriam. She had been adamant that Rosie should have a normal upbringing, that she should not go in to a children's home. If she knew Arthur had died, she might try and claim her back. She couldn't bear that to be the case.

"Can you tell me a bit about the birth mother?" She asked

"Oh, she was tall and slim with black hair and brown eyes. She was going out with the father for a couple of years. It wasn't just a casual fling."

"She was quite good looking then?"

What's that got to do with it Marjorie thought? The mother had agreed to give Rosie to her hadn't she? Why was she now being asked all these tortuous questions? She tried to change the subject.

"Do you mind what religion Rosie is brought up in? I gather the adoption agency can be quite fussy about that."

"It's in the Act." She replied irritably.

The children's officer paused for a moment and then leaned forward as she spoke to her, her eyes locking in to Marjorie's to gauge her response.

"People think they are being kind when they bring people together, as your friend has done. I'm sorry to hear she has passed away, so I can't meet her, but these people don't necessarily have experience in these matters. Take your case for example. Rosie now has no father and no brothers or sisters, just you. What is your annual income, I might ask?"

How rude Marjorie thought, her asking me that question. I suspect considerably better than yours.

"I don't know, I'll have to get back to you on that one." She said with retorted pride.

"I am sorry to ask this, but have you made any arrangements for Rosie in the case of your death?"

"I have arranged for my mother and a friend of mine who has a house in Richmond of her own to look after her."

"Marjorie, I don't have to state the obvious, but I am assuming your mother is in her seventies, and this friend of yours is single. This is hardly satisfactory is it?"

"My solicitors advised me to do this."

"Well if you can give me the name of your friend, I would like to go and see her if I may?"

"Of course."

"You do know that anyone looking after a child for a month or more has to inform the local authority?"

She said she didn't, but of course she did. If she'd informed the local authority, Rosie wouldn't be with her now. She would probably be with foster carers or in some children's home. The fact that Arthur had died would have seriously weighed against her. Her only option had been to lie low, wait for the authorities to come to her. Arthur had been taken away from her so unfairly in this life. They couldn't now take away Rosie or could they?

The adoption hearing on the 24th July was before a Judge Grant. Marjorie arrived with Rosie and was shown into a waiting room. The children's officer came, but not the solicitor. She stared at Marjorie in that knowing way as if to say, I've been here before. Marjorie did not know whether the hospital had informed her of the accident. She had been anxious to give the hospital as little information as possible, so as not to alert the authorities. There was another family before her. They were adopting a second child the Usher told her. Shortly afterwards they were shown in to the same room, where the Judge sat behind a table. There were several chairs facing him on the opposite side of the table. Straight away he said to Marjorie.

"I thought you were being represented?"

"I was, but my solicitor has not come yet."

He asked if she would like to wait for him and she said she would if it wasn't too inconvenient. He said that would be quite alright so she left the room. The children's officer stayed in. Marjorie wondered what conversation she was having with the judge in there. She made it clear in the meeting that she didn't approve of adoption particularly. Before long her solicitor came.

"Sorry I'm late. Trains were cancelled at Kings Cross so I had to hail a cab. Shall we go straight in ?"

The judge opened a file of papers on his desk and then took a sip of water from his glass. He made a note of who was representing whom. He then slowly turned the pages of a file of papers before him, nodding occasionally as he digested the contents. After a considerable silence, he raised his head and looked at Marjorie.

"Mrs Ronson, I'd like to say that I am entirely satisfied from the papers that I have read before me that you are giving Rosie a good home and every care."

He then paused and leant forward.

"However, I am not satisfied in this case that sufficient steps have been carried out to find the real birth mother."

Her solicitor got up to make some representations.

"My Lord, if I might draw you to the attention of page 5 and 6 of my affidavit, two letters have been written to the last know address in Danvers Road, one has been returned and one not replied to."

"That is not sufficient. I am prepared to grant temporary custody to Mrs Ronson whilst these steps are being taken. Has the client anything she wishes to say on this?"

Marjorie nervously got up to speak to the judge. Her hands were clammy. She caught the glance of the children's officer. She didn't know what she had told the Judge.

"If it please your Lordship, I feel to grant an adoption of Rosie would give her greater security, especially as she has no father. I don't think it should be delayed."

"It is precisely because she has no father, that I am reluctant to do anything until the birth mother is contacted, Mrs Ronson. I see no reason why such matters cannot be delayed until then. You certainly weren't precipitous yourself with this application, were you?" He said candidly.

"I'm sorry your Lordship, but there is a child living in the same road as her, that has said to her, where is her real mummy? I am worried that soon other people are going to say that sort of thing to her."

The Judge paused and exchanged glances with the children's officer. He said in no uncertain terms

"But you will tell her about her mother won't you?"

She hesitated, a little taken aback by the question

"Indeed I will, your Lordship. I liked the mother and will tell her all about her."

The Judge asked her lawyer what he thought and he said that he thought Marjorie should adopt Rosalie. The judge asked why and she couldn't remember what the lawyer said, except that Arthur's death was totally unexpected.

"I'm sorry for your loss, Mrs Ronson, but I am not satisfied that enough effort has been made in this case to find the birth mother. This is not your fault, but I would have liked to see more in the affidavit from your lawyer setting out the steps that have been taken to find her."

"Your Lordship, we did put advertisements as well in two North London papers," her lawyer interjected.

"That may be appropriate for announcing silly divorces, but this is a far more fundamental matter. We are talking about a child."

He said there should be an attempt made to trace her through the Ministry of Social Security. Her lawyer said he did not think they gave out addresses of people. The judge agreed, but said, they often forwarded letters.

"Mrs Ronson, I don't want you to feel that I am putting you off. I do intend to grant the adoption, subject to satisfactory enquiries and reports in due course. If I take a chance and grant it now, there is a danger that the mother could turn up in three or four years time and challenge it and say she had not given her formal consent and that adequate efforts had not been made to contact her."

He decided to hear the case again in six months time, not a year and assured Marjorie he was happy with her care of Rosie. He was granting her custody of her in the meantime.

"She's a lovely little girl." The judge said beaming at Rosie.

Outside the Court Marjorie chastised her lawyer.

"Why didn't you put more in your affidavit, as the judge asked? He was highly critical of you in there. You could have affected my chances."

"My apologies, Mrs Ronson, but it is in your interests to bide your time. I'm afraid we now have to do as the judge asks and contact the mother."

Marjorie sighed whilst pulling her overcoat around her shoulders.

"Miriam did say when I met her that if I ever needed to contact her, that if I sent a letter with her surname Sullivan-Cody to Cork, it would get to her as she is the only person with that surname in that area."

"Then lets try that then." Her lawyer replied.

"Wait," said Marjorie in a panic. "Miriam stressed that any letter sent should mention nothing about the baby, as it might be opened by the parents by mistake."

"Don't worry, we will be discreet."

And with that Marjorie walked with a heavy heart home thinking that once Miriam was contacted there was no knowing how she would react to Marjorie's situation.

MIRIAM 1969
MEDITERRANEAN

I N AUGUST 1969, whilst Miriam was on shore leave in Malta, she received out of the blue a telegram from a solicitor in London. It appeared that numerous attempts had been made to contact her in Ireland. If this was to do about Rosie, she hoped to God they hadn't contacted her parents.

Monro Pennefather& Co
Candlewick House
116 Cannon Street
London EC4
10th August 1969

Dear Madam
We would be grateful, if you could get in touch regarding a matter which arose on 4th September 1967. Perhaps you would be kind enough to telephone us or write to us at the above.

Yours sincerely
Monro Pennefather

She was out of her mind with worry as to whether Rosie was ill or something. All her feelings of bereavement returned. She'd told the lady she had given Rosie to, to be discreet, but to also contact her if anything happened to her baby. She desperately wanted to know she was alright. She would be nearly two now, old enough to walk and talk. She needed to see a photo of her.

She went to the nearest travel agent and asked if she could make an international phone call. The lady behind the desk said that they would charge her two shillings a minute for phone calls to England if that was alright. She didn't have much choice so she agreed.

After a number of rings the receptionist answered

"Monro Pennefather solicitors, can I help you?"

"I need to speak to David Munro."

"Can I ask who is calling?"

"Miriam Sullivan-Cody"

She could hear the line go dead as the receptionist put her on hold.

"Oh hello Miriam. I am glad you got in contact. Rosie is fine and doing well. Unfortunately Marjorie's husband died of a massive heart attack. Marjorie is doing well and would like to finalize the adoption process, as she is now quite attached to Rosie. Could you possibly write in with your contact details?"

"When did he die?" Miriam responded in a state of shock

"January 1968"

She quickly did the maths in her head. That means that Marjorie's husband died eight weeks after she had given her away. What was going on?

"I'm sorry, but you've taken all this time to tell me!" Miriam blurted out somewhat angrily.

"You have been rather difficult to contact."

She momentarily fell silent. Perhaps she had tried to contact her it was just that she had been on the cruise ship. Perhaps if she'd stayed in England she would have found out sooner. Now it would appear that her daughter was being brought up by a single mother which certainly had not been part of her original plan.

"Now that we have located you, where can we contact you if I don't mind asking?"

"I'm working on a cruise liner at present and won't be returning until 10th November, to Malta, where I have an apartment. I'll write in the meantime."

And with that she put the phone down. She slowly walked back to the apartment that she had just recently taken on with Lucy in Malta. They found this the perfect base for shore leave as they all spoke English in Malta and the apartments weren't that expensive. When she got back Lucy was preparing a small salad and some pasta for lunch. She was tossing the dressing in the salad bowl on the kitchen table.

"Good God, you look like you've seen a ghost!" She exclaimed as Miriam walked through the door.

"It feels like I have."

"Sit down. I'll get you a glass of vino to steady the nerves."

"I got this strange letter from a lawyer today. He was trying to be discreet, but I knew it was about my daughter because it referred to her birthday."

"Don't tell me something awful has happened!"

"No, not to her anyway, but the woman I gave her to lost her husband eight weeks after I gave her away. I can't believe she has waited nearly two years to tell me!"

Miriam placed her head in to her hands and Lucy put a comforting arm around her. She gently edged the glass of wine towards her on the table.

"Don't be too hard on yourself Miriam. You weren't to know this was going to happen. When you left the UK, you thought you had put in to place what was necessary for your daughter."

"I know, but if I'd found out sooner, would that have affected my decision? Probably yes."

"Maybe this lady thought she would lose this baby if she told you. She's already lost her husband. She probably needs your baby right now more than ever. Remember how you felt when your brother died?"

"You know what Lucy, if she had told me before, I could have taken Rosie back. I could have found a way." She said.

"You can't say that now," said Lucy. "Look, you didn't have a choice did you? The father wasn't interested and you couldn't have financially supported her."

"I know, but times are changing. This is nearly the 1970s for god's sake. Most women are now going on the pill and taking control of their lives, going to work, unlike their mothers did and still bringing up children."

"Well I think you should think long and hard Miriam, for the child's sake and for this woman's sake. Don't you think they have both suffered enough already?"

All Miriam could do was beat her fists against the table. The torment she felt inside was making her sick. All the memories of the birth came crashing down on her heart. Now, yet again, she was going to have to come to a decision.

She decided to write a letter to the solicitor asking for more information. She couldn't make a decision, based on her conversation with the solicitor. She realized she hardly knew this woman she had given her baby to nearly two years ago. What if she didn't have enough money now to support the baby? What if she had to go back to work?

She received her first letter from Marjorie in September, just before her second birthday. She confirmed that Rosie was doing well and that she loved the seaside. She said that her husband had died of a massive heart attack last year. She also said the Court had granted her custody for six months and now she wanted to apply for formal adoption.

"Why did the judge give her custody?" She asked Lucy

"Maybe to protect the interests of the child?"

Miriam wrote back to her with many searching questions. In her mind she was thinking, why had no one contacted her? Why had she given up her baby from one single mother to another? How could she now claim her back? She had deliberately left Marjorie and her husband alone so that she could bond with her baby. Now she felt betrayed. But having lost her elder brother last year, she knew she couldn't compound her bereavement, by taking Rosie. God knows she was suffering her own bereavement having lost her own child. That bereavement like the loss of a loved one never goes away.

She decided to hand in her notice at work, she couldn't stay on the cruise ship any longer. She needed to go back to London and sort this mess out.

"Whatever decision you make, make the right one for your child." Said Lucy.

They gave each other huge hugs and said they would stay in touch. Her flight back to the UK was with a heavy heart. In the letter Marjorie had sent her, were two photos of Rosie which she now kept close to her in her bag. One showed her eyes gazing questioningly at the camera. She wasn't particularly smiling in that photograph. The other showed her happily playing at the swimming pool. She looked so like Len it hurt.

When Miriam got back to London, it was like stepping back in time. She met up with her sister in Muswell Hill and her daughter Charlotte, who was nearly three now. She recounted the correspondence, she had had with Marjorie.

"The thing is sis, what else can you do? You can't take her back. You haven't got enough money to provide for her. Where are you going to work now?"

"I thought I would get a temporary job in Harrods for now. I am just so confused."

"Can I make a suggestion Miriam, I think you should go back to our parents in Cork for a few days. You will then realize the enormity of this secret that you have kept from them for so long. How do you think they would take it if they found out now? It would break their hearts. The Church would disown them. You gave away Rosie to protect them. To tell them now that they have another granddaughter that they haven't seen for two years is nothing short of suicide. Just because Marjorie's circumstances have changed it doesn't mean yours have!"

She knew her sister was right. Her heart was just so heavy with emotion right now.

"Listen I will forward any post that comes for you sis, just get the next ferry home."

"It's just seeing your daughter Charlotte is a constant reminder of what could have been. You never get over the loss of a child, having to give them up to someone else. You think of them constantly, bereaving their birthdays, bereaving their first steps, their first words. There is not a day I don't think about Rosie, the baby I never got to hold. Whenever I see another baby I weep inside."

"You need to hold this one together Miriam for yourself and Marjorie's sake."

MARJORIE 1969
LONDON

O N THE 2ND September 1969, Marjorie returned to London, having helped her mother move house in Margate to a smaller bungalow. Waiting for her was a letter from her lawyer, confirming that he had written to two addresses in Cork and also sent a letter via the Ministry of Social Security. Out of the blue, he had received a phone call from Miriam, in Malta. One of the Cork letters had reached her and she was very agitated. He asked her to let him have an address he could write to and said it concerned the adoption of Rosie. He sent Marjorie a copy of her letter to him dated 24th August 1969.

Sovereign Cruises
Malta

Dear Sirs

The particulars we discussed on the telephone can be sent to the given address. I am working on a liner cruising in the Mediterranean and shall not be returning to England before November 1st, but will be returning to Malta every 10 days within the next two months.

Since I received your letter yesterday, I have been out of my mind with worry as to whether the child was ill or something. I am very emotionally upset at the moment, so will need time to think.

During the last two years, I have not contacted the family, to enable them to feel real parental love for the child.

This has been extremely difficult for me at times, particularly on the 4th September and Christmas time.

I want the lady to write to me and assure me this child is really happy and I also want a photograph.

Her happiness is the most important thing and my decision shall be based on that.

Yours sincerely
M Sullivan-Cody

On the 2nd September, Marjorie wrote back to Miriam as follows

29 Dalmeny Road
Barnet

Dear Miriam

I have heard from the solicitors that they have succeeded in contacting you, and that you want to hear from me.

Rosalie is very well and a happy, friendly little girl. I enclose two photos, one of her at the Finchley swimming pool, where I have taken her many times this summer, there is a children's pool there, as she enjoys it so much. I also took her to Margate in June, and she loved the sands and playing in the sea. In the other photo she is with two children who live next door, *they've played a lot together this summer, and she is going to their birthdays tomorrow.*

My husband died of a heart attack in January last year. He loved Rosalie very much, and we treated her as our daughter in every way and I have continued to do so. My solicitors advised me to apply to adopt her early this year, and when the case came up the Judge emphasized that he was thoroughly satisfied with the home and care I was providing, but that further efforts must be made to trace you, and ask for your consent before he could grant an adoption. So he gave me custody of her, the case to come to court in six months. Perhaps you would like to telephone me, if so my number is 01 4493911.

Yours sincerely

Marjorie

After a fortnight Marjorie received a letter from Malta

Sovereign Cruises

Malta

Dear Mrs Ronson

Forgive me for taking so long in replying to your letter, but I needed time to get over the emotional state, I had been in for a week or so. I realize how anxious you are not to lose Rosalie, particularly by the tragedy of losing your husband. I was very upset on hearing this news and I do realize how much you must need Rosalie right now.

But what is best for the child is most important. I realize she loves you as her mother now and any interference from me would break both your hearts.

But she is still part of me and I feel great concern before I make this final decision to know if you can still support her in the manner you would have done if your husband was alive. I realize the Court must have confidence in you to consider this situation.

But now I feel I must know more and be assured that I am making the right decision.

Over the past 2 years I have thought many times of how quickly I handed Rosalie over to you, with really not knowing enough about you. I realize this is entirely my fault, but I was impressed by you and felt you really wanted a child so much.

I am sorry to keep you waiting for so long, but I do not want to make a rash decision this time because of sentiment, and thereafter wonder throughout my life if she is really happy.

So if you can tell me what plans you have for her, if it will be necessary for you to work to support her, and this is something I don't like to make a point of, but I think it's necessary. If anything happened to you, what then?

Please assure me Mrs Ronson and don't let me hurt you.

My love to you both

Miriam

Marjorie wrote to her on the "3rd September answering her questions

29 Dalmeny Road

Barnet

Dear Miriam

Thank you very much for your letter, I realize you want to be sure that Rosalie is happy and well provided for before you

make a decision.

I assure you that she is really happy and lively, and making good progress. The Court was satisfied about this and they do investigate thoroughly before they decide

My husband was comfortably off when he died, and I receive an income from his estate. Because he made this good provision, I am free to look after Rosie myself, and do not go out to work, and shall not need to do so. I am making enquiries about primary schools in the neighbourhood, so as to decide which will be best for her, and get her name down in good time. I have also made arrangements in my Will for her to be cared for should I die, and made financial provision for this. The Court was satisfied on this point.

I fully agree with you that what is best for Rosalie is the most important thing. I can only say that I love and care for her, as my husband and I did from the start, and as I have done during the 20 months since he died. It would have been easier simply to continue in this way, but it would provide Rosalie with greater security to be legally adopted. So I do hope you will feel able to consent to this."

Marjorie

Marjorie waited 4 weeks for a reply from Miriam, and nothing came so she wrote a brief note asking for a reply. Finally almost seven weeks after she sent her letter in answer to hers, she heard from her in a letter posted in Cork.

Macroom

Cork

Dear Mrs Ronson

I am sorry for the delay in writing.

I did not receive your letters until 2 weeks ago as we by-passed Malta due to bad weather, and then I know it was selfish, but I needed time to think.

I have decided I will agree to the adoption, but if anything should happen to you, the child must be given my address should she wish to contact me.

The most worrying thing in making this decision is that factor. I should hate to think that she may one day end up in an orphanage.

I hope you have a long and happy life and I am sure you will make a good mother. Please send the papers C/O Mrs Barney, 13 Mount View Road, London N4, as I shall return to London Tuesday 11th November.

God Bless you both
Love Miriam

Marjorie couldn't believe it! Her prayers had finally been answered. She had agreed in principle to an adoption, all she needed to do now was get her to sign the consent forms.

On 5th September, she received a visit from the children's officer. She told her that Miriam had been contacted, and she seemed very glad, saying she expected the mother would give her consent, and even if she didn't it would almost certainly be waived. She talked once more, about why she thought an adoption order was unnecessary. They were sat at the kitchen table sipping their cups of tea.

"Marjorie, it is the relationship with the child that is important, not whether or not the child is adopted. I must say I am highly critical of the delay you instigated in not letting the mother know your change of circumstances. This child may well grow up wanting to contact her real parents."

"It is because of the anxiety that I have suffered, that I want to adopt her. I feel my anxiety will reflect on Rosie, if I don't."

"You must divorce the emotions you had for your husband from the emotions you have for Rosie. It is the mother and child relationship which is important."

Marjorie said if she were not adopted, she would be caused embarrassment whenever she had to produce a birth certificate, and it was in a different name to the one she was known by. The children's officer said

"But this will only be three times in her life Marjorie."

In her letter from Cork Miriam had said she would be coming over to stay with her sister Orla at 13 Mount View Road London N4 on the 11th November. Marjorie rang up her lawyer as she thought this would be the perfect opportunity to send Miriam the consent forms. She also thought it would be a good idea to go and see Miriam, before the children's officer descended on her as she needed to forewarn her that the children's officer knew absolutely nothing about Mrs Bangerter.

She went round to Mount View Road, but on sounding the door bell there was no answer. She checked through the letter box and there seemed to be no one at home so she scribbled a note for her to call her that evening when she returned and dropped it through the front door.

That evening she phoned. She seemed a little agitated and said she couldn't talk for long, but was there a problem?

"No no problem. I just wanted to forewarn you that I didn't tell the children's officer in this case about Mrs Bangerter's involvement. I said a friend of mine who has since died, put me in contact with you. You don't mind do you? I'd hate to see her get in to trouble."

"No I wouldn't want her to get into trouble either." She paused. Marjorie could hear a child running about in the background.

"I suppose you've also rung me about the consent forms that you want me to sign?"

"Yes."

"Listen, I will do everything I can do to help, but I'm a bit tied up with job interviews at the moment as I need to get a job."

Marjorie felt she didn't seem to grab the urgency of the situation or maybe she was having second thoughts. It was one thing to agree to an adoption in a letter. Marjorie knew the birth mother had the right to change her mind right up to when the adoption order was made.

"What job interviews are you going for tomorrow?"

"Well I am going back to do an interview at Harrods where I've worked before."

"Can't you go to the Court first, as it's not far from where you are staying?"

"I have to get a job Marjorie," she said slightly irritably. "I'll miss the interview if I go to Court first."

Marjorie didn't receive a further phone call from her for about a week. She wondered if she was now having second thoughts about the adoption. Her lawyer said he hadn't heard anything.

She did ring eventually to confirm that she had started a job at Harrods, but had decided to leave as the pay was lousy. She was starting a new job in a pub in Knightsbridge on the Monday and had got the morning off on the Wednesday, so would go and sign the papers at Barnet then and ring afterwards. She said she had left her sister's. Marjorie asked where she was staying now and she confirmed that she was staying at a hotel in Paddington, although she was still looking for a flat.

She rang the following Wednesday.

"Hi Marjorie, Miriam here. I have been to Court to sign the papers, but the birth certificate wasn't there."

"But if the birth certificate wasn't there, then the consent is not valid." She could hear herself wail.

"It's not my problem the lawyer didn't sort it out!"

Marjorie put the phone down and waited for the children's officer to call. She said she was going to see Miriam that evening and she just prayed that this mess would be sorted out then. She made herself a strong black coffee to steady her nerves and took out a chocolate digestive biscuit from the tin. Sure enough the phone rang an hour later.

"Hello Marjorie, it's Mrs Barnet here. I had Miss Sullivan-Cody here about half an hour ago. She apologized for the trouble she has caused. I think we had a good interview."

What did that mean she thought to herself, bearing in mind Mrs Barnet's views on adoption?

" Miriam has given me her sister's addresses. She says she still hasn't received a letter from the Court asking her if she would like to attend, and I've told her I'll get the Court to send her one."

"If Miriam has signed the papers and given her consent, then surely she doesn't have the right to turn up at Court at the last minute and oppose it?" Marjorie said.

She was terrified that she would see Rosie and want her back. She hadn't exactly been forthcoming in signing the consent form.

"Miriam is still a very confused lady. She is entitled to turn up at court and give her side of the story. I doubt she will oppose it, but most people like to think they can."

At the end of the week Marjorie received notification from Barnet County court that the hearing would be on 8th January 1970 at 10.30 am.

The Children's officer came to see her about a week before the case came up.

"I've had a meeting with Miriam. She was a little tearful, I'm afraid. She can't get over the fact that the father isn't interested in either her or the baby. She said he paid for all the expenses at the time of the birth and that was that. She wants to know whether the Consent form is necessary for the adoption?"

"She's not going to oppose it is she?"

"I don't know Marjorie. She talked a lot about Rosie's father, the fact that he was interested in the theatre and making money. I told her the consent form was not necessary for the adoption but obviously it would help. She decided to give me her parent's address."

"Why? She has always told me that her parents are never to be contacted!"

"She seemed worried about what would happen to Rosie, if you died."

"But I've told her that I've made arrangements for that."

"Yes she knows, but she felt it would be an extra safeguard, if I knew how to get in contact with her. I probably won't know if you die, but rest assured, I think Miriam is more taken up with her emotions at the moment."

Marjorie hoped these emotions weren't for Rosie.

When the hearing date finally came on the 8th January, Marjorie made her way to Barnet County Court in the freezing cold with Rosie wrapped up in a warm, smart red woollen coat, with gloves and scarf to match. She did not see the woman standing across the road looking at her dressed forlornly in black beneath a bus shelter. Little did she know this was Miriam longing to see Rosie's face and touch her baby. Tears were coursing down her face.

As she got to the Courthouse her lawyer was already standing at the entrance. He ushered her inside and guided her to the board with the Court Circular on it.

"It looks as if we are in Court 4 today which is the fourth along on the ground floor. Do you fancy grabbing a cup of tea first? We are still waiting for the children's officer to arrive?"

"Do you think it will be alright this time?"

"I see no reason why not. I don't see any sign of the mother, yet."

The children's officer, Mrs Barnet arrived whilst they were drinking their cups of tea and they all agreed it was time to go in front of the Judge. They approached the usher who ushered them into Court 4 before Judge Grant.

"All rise"

His Lordship entered and everyone in the room bowed. There were two barristers in gowns and wigs sitting in front of them, one represented by the local authority and one instructed by her solicitor, called Mr Bentham QC.

"If it please your Lordship."

"Can we dispense with the formalities my good counsel. We have a child present, who unless her intention is to become a lawyer will not benefit from such theatre." said the Judge dismissively.

" My Lord since we were last before you, significant and I might say fruitful attempts have been made in this case, to locate the birth mother. Your Lordship may recall that when we were last before your Lordship, you were satisfied with the care Rosie was receiving in this case, but nevertheless, the mother should be informed of Mrs Ronson's change in circumstances."

"Yes."

"I am happy to report my Lord that the mother has agreed to an adoption in the form of a letter to the applicant. May I refer your lordship to exhibit A of the applicant's affidavit."

"Yes, I have it here in front of me."

"My lord, the birth mother did also attempt to lodge the consent form at the Court but unfortunately the Court had not retained a copy of the birth certificate."

"A case of pilot error, I take it?"

"Yes my Lord."

"Has the mother been invited to make an appearance today, Mr Bentham."

"Yes she has, my Lord and as you can see she has not shown to appear."

"Very well."

The judge asked the lawyer if everything had been tied up and he said it had. He then turned to Marjorie and said.

"I'm sure you will cope single-handed, manfully, that's the wrong word, but if you need help at any time you will ask ?"

"I will," she said. But she didn't need anyone's help or anyone interfering. She wanted to move on. She had had enough of that from the children's officer.

"And you must not look upon her as compensation for your own loss. That must be a temptation sometimes, but you must let her have her freedom."

"Of course I will."

"And you have friends?"

She said she had. He turned to the children's officer and asked if she was satisfied with everything and she said she was. Marjorie was relieved.

The Judge handed a tin of sweets across, lovely big wrapped chocolates. The children's officer told Marjorie to take two. Rosie chewed one and Marjorie put the other in her pocket.

"Mrs Ronson, having considered all the evidence before me, and the mother's acceptance of the situation, I am prepared to agree to the adoption."

Oh My God, Marjorie couldn't believe it. All this time she thought the odds had been stacked against her, that she might lose the only precious thing she had left which was Rosie. Even then she couldn't quite believe it that Miriam hadn't turned up at the last minute. The Judge got up and came down towards Rosie.

"What lovely pink cheeks she's got, have you been pinching them to make them pink?"

"They are always like that." Marjorie said proudly.

"You're a lovely little girl."

He then bent down and held out his hand to her. She put hers in his and he held it a few seconds, looking at her and she smiled up at him and wrinkled her nose. He said again.

"You are a lovely little girl."

Then he said to Marjorie.

"She'll bring you much joy."

He turned to the children's officer and said.

"You're still looking for a new children's officer aren't you?"

"Yes we are." She said.

"I might apply you know." He said grinning.

"We're looking for someone really first class."

"Oh I'd better not apply then." He beamed.

They then went outside and Marjorie's lawyer remarked on what a human judge he was. She didn't notice that the lady in black had now disappeared, unable to cope with the trauma of never seeing her little girl again. Now she had to move on with her life as Rosie had to move on with hers with Marjorie.

ROSIE 1970s
LONDON

ROSIE REMEMBERED BEING left at the gates on her first day at school. She was clutching this letter that her adoptive mother had given her in her hand on a small piece paper.

My Dear Rosie

I am writing this in case I die when you are still little, before I have been able to tell you how I came to adopt you.

When Daddy and I married it was a second marriage for both of us. We had each been married to someone else, and those marriages ended in divorce. I had no children in my first marriage, but daddy had two sons, Michael and John. Daddy and I met some years after our first marriages ended, and fell in love, and we were married on 11th July 1966, when I was 44 and Daddy was 53. We longed for a baby, but we did not have one. Forty is rather late for a woman to have her first baby. So we decided to adopt one. When we applied to several Adoption Societies they would not accept us, because they have so many people wanting babies they will not consider anyone over 40.

Then I met your mother whose name is Miriam Sullivan-Cody, through a friend of mine. Miriam had been very friendly for a year or so with your father whose name is Leonard Jackson. She hoped they would marry, but this did not happen, so she had no home for you, and would have to work to earn money. She thought it over very carefully, and decided it would be better for you to be adopted by someone who wanted a baby very much, and could provide you with a real home. So, when you were a tiny baby you came to us, and we loved you as our very own. Daddy often gave you your bottle and your feeds, and I am enclosing a photo of you with him when you were about two months old and one with me. We took them on a bright sunny November morning. We planned to look after you for some months and then apply to adopt you. In the meantime you thrived and we were all very happy.

Then on a Monday morning, 15th January 1968, Daddy had a heart attack at the office. He was rushed to Barts Hospital. Gran came to stay with me to look after you while I went to see him each day. He slowly recovered, and was allowed out of bed a bit longer each day, and one day Gran and I took you to see him at the hospital. On Sunday 28th January he got worse and had another heart attack, and he died in the evening of Monday 29th January.

It was tragic, and I won't try to describe it to you. After some weeks I went to daddy's solicitor to ask how I could adopt you. He told me to wait until 18 months old, and then apply. This I did. We contacted your mother, and she gave her consent and I finally adopted you on 8th January 1970. The adoption was granted at Barnet County Court by Judge Grant, who was kind and gave you two big chocolates.

I shall now tell you all I can about your original parents. I met Miriam Sullivan-Cody and liked her. She was tall, slim with black hair and brown eyes. Her parent's home was Cork, and her mother was Irish, her father English and she had several brothers and sisters. She was at the time a Dress Designer. She told me that Leonard Jackson was British/South African, born in England and brought up in South Africa. He was tall, blond and blue eyed. He was a Company Director in Dublin and came to London quite often. He was a keen businessman and fond of the theatre.

I am typing this because ink might fade. I am leaving it in safe keeping with Mr R.M. Ritchie of Trower Still & Keeling, 5 New Square, Lincoln's Inn London WC2. He is my solicitor and if when you are older you want advice about your affairs, I'm sure he would help you.

I have appointed Gran and Aunty Joy to be your guardians and left some money to pay for what you will need until you are grown up. I hope darling that you will settle and be happy and make the most of your life.

Marjorie

"Enjoy your first day at school darling."

She shuffled off to the classroom, which was full of rows of small wooden desks. She found herself a table and sat down. Gradually the other pupils began to arrive. Some emptied the contents of their satchels out onto the tables. She tucked away the letter in her pocket.

The teacher walked into the classroom. She was wearing a light green shift dress with a matching cardigan. Her blonde hair was held back by a green grip.

"Now children, settle down."

They all sat down and gazed at this woman in authority. Her desk was larger than the others, with a small bunch of peonies, in a vase on the left. Behind her hung a huge large blackboard with some sums on it.

"My name is Miss Price and I am going to be your Form teacher for Year One."

Being her first day of school, she was slightly nervous like the rest of the pupils. She shifted about in her seat, which was a little uncomfortable. She laid her ruler and pencils on the groove in front of her.

"I would like you as your first exercise today, to draw a picture of your family. You can include pets if you like."

The teacher handed out some pieces of paper and gave them some colouring crayons. The light shone through the classroom windows, casting a shadow over the piano in the corner.

Panic started to rise up in her throat. She hastily looked round the classroom to see if anyone had noticed her reaction. Her palms felt all clammy. She had no one to draw but her adoptive mother, and by judging from the other mothers she'd seen dropping off the other kids, a mother that was considerably older than the other mothers. Now she'd found out she'd got two mothers. She couldn't out of love for her adoptive mother admit she wasn't her real mother. She constantly reminded Rosie that she was even more loved than most children because she had chosen her. She was so confused. Why had her mother chosen to tell her on her first day of school that she was adopted? It didn't make any sense. How could she fit in with these children who came from proper families? The tears just started welling up and streaming down her face.

"Whatever is the matter Rosie?" the teacher asked bending over her to place a hand on her shoulder.

She started heaving. The other pupils couldn't stop staring. They didn't know what to make of her sudden outburst and most of them held their pencils in mid flow waiting for Miss Price to bark her next orders.

"Let me take you over to the corner by the piano. We can talk more privately there."

She pushed the chair backwards and tentatively walked towards the piano. The teacher came over and gave her a small hug. She never had that sort of hug at home, she thought.

"Now tell me what's upsetting you?"

She couldn't blurt out what was really upsetting her. The words just wouldn't come out. She hadn't had time to sort it out in her own mind yet, how she had started out as a one parent family when most had two, to now, a two mother one.

"My daddy died when I was a baby."

She didn't really have a concept of death at that age she just knew it made her adoptive mother unhappy that her father had died, except as it transpired, he wasn't her father either.

"Oh I am so sorry. How insensitive of me. Here's a tissue to wipe your eyes with."

She wiped her eyes and blew her nose. She couldn't tell her what she really wanted to tell her, that her mummy wasn't her real mummy, that even at a young age she had realized she didn't have anything in common with her. Not only did she not look like her, she didn't feel like her.

"How about I have a quiet word with mummy when she picks you up from school?"

Oh no she thought. She wasn't sure she was ready for her to announce to the world that she was adopted. They never spoke about it in public.

"I don't want to upset mummy."

The teacher told Rosie to calm down. She could feel the other children watching her, slightly bewildered by the whole incident.

"I suggest you stay here by the piano, while the others continue. Perhaps you would like to sort out the building blocks in the play box for when you start to feel better."

She sat down on the floor and began to assemble the wooden bricks together. What a mess she had made of her first day at school and what would her mother say? All she knew is that she wished she came from a normal family like all the other children in her class.

That day her adoptive mother picked her up from the school gates and Miss Price came over. She told her mother that it had been a bit fractious on the first day, but that she was sure she'd settle into school life soon.

"She looks so like you Marjorie."

Her adoptive mother beamed in response. No she doesn't, Rosie thought. She looks nothing like her. Even her mannerisms didn't fall in to sink with her own. She made her hair short when she wanted it long. She made her wear boys clothes when she wanted dresses.

They drove home in silence in her beloved mini. All the other children were picked up in smart new motors. Why did her adoptive mother have to drive a clapped out mini?

She couldn't attach any blame to her adoptive mother for the situation they found themselves in. She was only a child at the time. From the outset she had been honest with her and though no one relishes the prospect of being adopted, she supposed she ought to be thankful for that.

In many ways she had a privileged upbringing. She was brought up in suburbia North London, in a nice detached house close to her school. In those days they were entitled to a freedom that we can little afford our children today. She would cycle to the park with her friends and play imaginary worlds at home. She was an only child and so spent a lot of her childhood on her own with her adoptive mother for company. She would encourage her to go out and make friends, something she neither had the confidence or the competence to do herself. As a result, she grew up a confident person with all the insecurities of adoption.

It wasn't just that she was adopted, It was the fact that her adoptive mother came from a different era. Her adoptive mother had grown up with the insecurities of a child showered with love. With her adoptive mother it was just Rosie and her. She was the artistic one who loved to design and draw. She wanted to listen to contemporary music, which had rhythm and soul. Her adoptive mother would be drawn to classical things, things from a bygone era.

Christmas was a difficult time because her adoptive mother had no family to speak of. Maybe it was the Irish in her, but she longed for Christmas to be a more gregarious social affair.

She was required to change schools three times as a result of moving houses, before her adoptive mother settled on a private school in North London. This was when she was introduced to music. The school bus which took an hour at least used to play Radio 1 at full blast to and from school. Until then she had been subjected to Radio 4 and the odd bit of classical music. By the end of her first year, she had got herself a best friend. She was from a largely dysfunctional family with five brothers and a sister. She was no more embarrassed by her family than Rosie's. They weren't the wealthiest kids in school, but that suited them fine. Many of their friends wore Rolexes and Cartier rings to school. Some had holiday homes in Marbella. They were content to take the Underground to Oxford Circus and stroll around Top Shop for hours on end.

On one such Saturday, they were on one of these outings in the West End. They hopped off at Oxford Circus Tube Station and mounted the escalators. They were both very skinny, wearing the shortest skirts they could get away with. As they burst out in to the sunshine and the crowded street on the Circus, her friend said.

"I fancy going to Our Price, by Bond Street. There's a new single out called "Tainted Love by Soft Cell, I really want to get it."

"OK then. I fancy the new Spandau Ballet single."

They edged along Oxford Street negotiating the people coming in the opposite direction. She loved coming to the West End to browse through all the latest fashion shops and record shops. Everything seemed so fast when you came in to Central London. People to see, places to go.

"It's very busy here today. Where do all these people come from?" She asked.

"Beats going to Brent Cross though. It's so much cooler."

Suddenly there was loud explosion. It shook the whole street. They could hear the sound of shattered glass in the distance.

"What was that?"

"I think it's coming from the Wimpy. Look down there."

She strained her neck to see the damage over the mass of people. There were flames coming out of the glass fronted restaurant. Slowly screaming and hysteria set in. People started running about everywhere. Then sirens came as hundreds of Police Officers descended on them.

"I think we'd better get out of here Rosie!" her friend screamed.

"Do you know how?"

"Lets start walking towards Baker Street."

They grabbed each others hands and made a dive for the nearest side street. They could now feel the pressure of the people pushing behind them. Everybody was desperate to get out of the disaster zone. They were only young and to be honest, quite lost down those side streets.

"Are you alright girls?" a policeman asked them.

"Yes we're OK" Rosie said. "What happened?"

"Suspected IRA bomb miss. Blown up the Wimpy Bar. It's not safe here right now. I suggest you get as far away from the scene as you can."

They trudged up Baker Street and then past Regent's Park on their right. They then carried on walking to Swiss Cottage. They were exhausted, but at least they were safe.

"I think we had a narrow escape there Rosie. We could have been killed!"

Yes she thought, killed by her irish ancestors, no doubt. She still hadn't told any of her friends that she was adopted. She hadn't met anybody else in the same situation and she knew that she couldn't really start doing anything about it until she was older.

Another friend she made at the time was on the school bus. She invited her to go and stay at her family's time share in Mijas Costa, just outside Marbella in Spain. She envied her normal family. They spent a lot of time in Puerto Banus and the then newly built Sotogrande where another friend of theirs had a luxury apartment.

One day they walked along the quay at Puerto Banus, gazing at the white washed houses tumbling in to the sea. The boats were moored up in the harbour and there were plenty of well groomed people from the jet set parading the restaurants. These were people who were proud to be seen, unlike her adoptive mother who liked nothing more than to stay holed up at their house. They very rarely had anyone come over to visit and on the rare occasions they did it was usually just one person such as her Aunty Joy or her Uncle Charles. Her adoptive mother did not like social confrontations at all and certainly wouldn't be seen in fashionable places for fashion's sake.

"I wouldn't mind having nice things one day."

"Me too."

Her friend was lucky to have a mum and dad, she thought. She didn't come from a dysfunctional family.

"Aren't you glad that your parents are still together?" She asked her one day when they were sipping their cokes at a bar.

"God no! I'm the only one in my class who doesn't have divorced parents."

That was part of the problem. She knew lots of people whose parents had separated or were going through a divorce.

There wasn't a day that went by during those years that she didn't think about contacting her real mother. Her adoptive mother was now in her sixties. Her dilemma was how would this affect her adoptive mother? Even though her adoptive mother had met her real mother, she never told her much about her. She did tell her that when her father died that her real mother had threatened to take her back.

By this time in her life she had stopped bringing friends home, preferring to see them on their own turf, so she wouldn't have to suffer any embarrassment. Despite moving house many times her adoptive mother would always manage to make the property look like something out of the dark ages. The same ancient furniture would be installed. She had no time for interior design. She would delight in appliances if they didn't work marvelling on the fact that she was useless with technology. In contrast her friend's parents were proud when they redecorated their homes with new curtains and fabrics and new furniture. She knew her adoptive mother was not normal in this respect. The advent of television had helped in that aspect.

Her adoptive mother was older now and her eccentric behavior was even more enhanced. She didn't care that lots of people thought they were doing a favour to someone when they were adopting them. The reality was very different. She knew that her inherent genetic make up was different. You didn't adopt the practices of your adoptive parents, you yearned to find the true you.

One morning her adoptive mother and Rosie were sitting at the breakfast bar at their house they had moved to in North London.

She used to dread these mornings. Her adoptive mother would often turn off Radio 4 when she sat down, leaving them to stare at the blank wall with a spot light, casting a shadow in the silence. She could hear a pin drop on these mornings, whilst her mother was crunching her toast.

"You know, you can always contact your real mother, Miriam, when you are eighteen, don't you darling? I know it seems a long way away, but I wouldn't mind."

"I don't need to mum."

She never spoke much of it again. She knew to do so would destroy her. She wasn't sure that if she started the process, that she would like what she saw. She didn't know if her parents had remarried or had families of their own. Looking back, whilst she had been given the barest information about her parents, she hadn't been told the whole story. Had she been, she would have been in contact.

MIRIAM 1970s
IRELAND

"SO MIRIAM, WHAT do you think of my proposition?"

She was sat up curled on David's sofa in a dingy dressing room behind the stage. The floors were wooden and worn. The place smelt of sweat and talcum powder. This was the retreat the ballerinas would come to when they wanted to moan about the evenings' performance. David was a tough choreographer and only expected the best from his dancers. At the moment they were performing his rendition of the Nutcracker. After months of rehearsals, they were finally going to perform their first show. The door would open and slam shut as dancers would come in to ask for last minute ribbons for their shoes.

"I don't know David," she said, dragging on a cigarette and taking a small sip from a glass of whisky that David had given her.

"I've only just got started. At the moment, I have four girls working for me, but what you are asking me to take on is fourteen costumes for five different scenes for next season, which is going to take months to get right!"

"Listen Miriam, I know you can rise to the challenge. This could be the making of you."

She knew instinctively what he was saying made sense. Since the adoption, she had decided not to go back to the cruise ships. There was no point in running away from things forever. Neither could she stay in London. She couldn't afford or bear to be in the same city as her daughter. The memories were too painful. Ireland was her real home. She had decided to take on a small flat in Cork, just off Hanover Square. She had then advertised for four seamstresses on the promise that David would provide her with some freelance work to start off with from the theatre. After each rave review, David's profile was getting bigger and bigger as were the demands for more costumes. She was excited if not a little daunted by the challenge. She poured herself another whisky.

"Can you persuade the company to give me some form of advance? That way I can keep my head above water and give you the best I've got."

David was rummaging round in the drawers on his dressing table, trying to find the manuscript.

"There it is!" he exclaimed throwing his gesticulated fingers in the air and then promptly plunging himself on the sofa beside Miriam with theatrical abandon. He then grabbed her whisky tumbler and put it on the table beside him.

"That's what I like about you Miriam. You always want to drive a hard bargain." He retorted with a giggle.

"Perhaps, if you could just rustle up some drawings for us, I can show them to the board and put a financial proposal to you. You know I chose you because I believe in you."

She smiled. David even though he was gay, had always had a soft spot for her. Ever since her demise with the pregnancy he had made sure that she was well looked after. He never asked any questions. She thought he just assumed she had, had an abortion. He had rustled up a sinking fun, which he had sent to her in London. She had never used that money, preferring to give that to her sister so she could buy clothes for Charlotte. Ever since her return to Ireland, he had been instrumental in inspiring her to set up the dressmakers.

Suddenly the door burst open and the frailest of dancers waltzed by, shimmering in her ballet costume.

"We're on in five minutes David."

"I'd better go Miriam. See you backstage, when the performance finishes."

"Break a leg."

She didn't need to see the performance as she'd seen it many times before. It always amazed her how moving ballet could be. The music would sometimes bring tears to your eyes when you least expected it. The gentle hum of the Orchestra before the performance to a crescendo at the end. Each instrument, playing its' own part. The sets were always breathtaking and the ballet dancers, so graceful. She longed to be able to dance like those dancers. Their frames were so fragile. She swore she never saw them eat anything. The male dancers, of course were heavily vetted by David. They would never fail in their loyalty to him.

Whilst Miriam sat back stage, she could feel the tension of the cast, as they carried out every change of scene. There would be a lot of shouting and screaming going on. She tended to stay out of David's way, as she knew tempers would get frayed. Whilst the audience would see an effortless performance, there would always be some slip up that the cast made sure was never spotted. The endless changes in costume, meant that whatever she designed for them, would have to be durable and able to last many performances. They would also have to be in a pliable fabric to allow the dancers to breath.

She took out a sketch book from her art case and sharpened a few pencils. She idly drew the silhouette of a dancer and then started to shade the arms and legs. For the first costume she decided to wrap the dancer in waves of chiffon, adding a bow at the back at the base of the spine. For the second, she drew the shortest butterfly skirt with an embroidered pattern around the rim. David popped in briefly between acts.

"I like those," he said bending over the sketch pad. "The more avant-garde, the better."

She continued to draw more dancers, as the performance wore on. Inspired by the music, which she could hear in the background, she drew some pictures of male dancers in skin tight costumes. She would become completely lost in those drawings, as if time stood still. By the time she had completed the last drawing, she could hear the thunder of applause from the audience.

"It's a wrap darling!" David exclaimed, as he burst in to the dressing room, a myriad of dancers still passing him in the corridor.

"Let's go and celebrate!"

By now it was just past 11 o'clock. The only bar still open was a small pub around the corner, where all the cast used to hang out after the performance. Miriam grabbed her coat and her drawings and applied some lipstick. David picked up his keys and a packet of thin cigars. After shouting various orders out at everybody and at the same time offering his congratulations, he put his arm around her and led her out of the stage door. There were a few flash photographers outside getting photographs for the next morning's Irish Times.

"That will give them something to talk about!" he laughed, as they entered the crowded pub next door. "If only they knew!"

They sat down in the corner and the barman brought them a bucket of champagne.

"To us," he exclaimed as they clinked their flutes.

From that night on she buried herself in her drawings. If she was happy with a design she had come up with, she would take a piece of fabric and cut out a design to the drawing. She would then sew it together on her Singer sewing machine. When she was satisfied, she would take it to one of her girls who would come and work at her apartment and they would put together the prototype. David got her an advance of six hundred pounds, which was more than enough to start off with. Sometimes, he would pass by on his way to a performance and see how they were getting on. He nearly always approved of the costumes they were making and would only criticize if he thought the fabric was too heavy or uncomfortable for the dancers. Their first commission was for Swan Lake. In some respects this was an easy commission because they couldn't depart from the classical theme. However they only had six weeks to produce sixteen costumes for four acts.

"Don't worry darling. Whatever the costume, it is the dancer's responsibility to pull off the performance."

"I know, I just want the production to be perfect."

"If you make a mistake, it won't stop me commissioning you."

There were mistakes. On that first performance Miriam suffered what could only be considered a dressmaker's nightmare. As she sat in the audience, looking at the dancers, all the costumes started coming apart because she simply hadn't put enough gusset in the tight chiffon sleeves.

"I'm so sorry David. One of my dressmakers was not good enough." She exclaimed.

"Oh don't be silly, darling, the audience loved it. It is the first time a tragedy has turned in to a comedy. I've never laughed so much in years."

Over time she went on to design for most of David's productions which were now taking him further afield to Dublin and London.

One Saturday morning she was sitting in the kitchen nursing a mug of coffee, when she heard the phone ring.

"Hi Miriam, it's me David. I've got a fantastic commission for you. I had to use all my powers of persuasion though."

"Oh David, don't tease me."

"You've only got to design the entire costumes for the latest production of " The Boyfriend" at the Everyman Theatre in London!"

"Holy Mother of God, you didn't tell me you had pitched me on that one! I thought they would give that commission to someone like Tony Kelly!"

"You get absolute artistic license to do what you want. There are 1920s bathing costumes, Norfolk jackets, scanty bikinis. The world is your oyster. I don't need to tell you the pay is fantastic."

That weekend, she worked again day and night on the drawings. She didn't stop to listen to the radio or watch the television. Her mind was bursting with enthusiasm. Every detail had to be authentic. This era was her grandparent's era, a time of optimism, just after the First World War, in some ways a decadent one. She grabbed some paints from the cupboard and began colouring the costumes in a myriad of colours. The swimsuits had to be fun and cheeky, the evening dresses had to sparkle with encrusted diamante.

The following week she hired some seamstresses to help her and they set about making the costumes. They ordered swathes of fabric in beautiful pastel shades, complimented by the sharp contrast of navy ribbon.

As was her way now, she would totally immerse herself in her work. There was no room in her heart for anyone else. She couldn't bear to be alone with her thoughts for fear they would consume her. She had heard that Len had gone and emigrated to South Africa. A part of her wanted to show him how successful she had managed to become on her own, and even though she knew she couldn't contact her daughter perhaps she would contact her. Surely Marjorie would have given her daughter her name by now? Her surname was unusual so it couldn't take long for her to put two and two together.

"You're a star!" exclaimed David, when she next saw him. "The production absolutely love what you have come up with."

They were sitting outside a café on Sunday morning in Dublin, overlooking Trinity college. The sun was breaking through the trees and David had just ordered them two coffees. He threw the Sunday papers down on the coffee table in front of them.

"Take a look at these reviews, I quote "Designer for The Boyfriend" David Gordon decided to use all his powers of persuasion which are considerable to coax a very good friend and costume designer of noted ability and flair to take on the task."

"Oh David, stop talking so loudly. People are starting to stare."

"Oh let them. I go on. This was none other than Miriam Sullivan-Cody, Cork born, London trained and established in her own fashion business in Cork City for over ten years, also a direct descendant of the renowned "Bufallo Bill Cody". Some years before, Miriam had designed and made costumes for the Irish Ballet Company which was choreographed by David Gordon and they had received high praise. Though exceedingly busy, working at high pressure, Miriam generously consented to take on the heavy task."

"It wasn't that heavy, I loved doing it!"

The waitress came over with their coffees and a glass of water each. Miriam carefully spooned two sugar cubes in to her cup and waved David to continue. She enjoyed basking in David's enthusiasm and adulation at the same time.

"And heavy it is indeed, as the cast numbers eighteen and each requires at least two changes of costume. Working at every available minute, Miriam has dreamed up a complete range of some of the most delightful, colourful and beautifully made costumes that are likely to be seen on a London stage for some time."

"Oh David does it really say that?" as she leaned over pulling her cardigan tightly round her shoulders.

"I go on. Included in the numbers are bathing suits of the period which add a special and very authentic note, capturing the spirit of their times and yet hilariously funny to the modern eye now long accustomed to the scanty bikini. There are additionally costumes for the fancy dress ball which in themselves, are a complete delight giving Miriam a chance to show off her rare genius for the exotic."

"At this moment she nearly choked on her coffee. Exotic!"

"I haven't finished yet. She has even designed and executed a marvellous "Plus Fours" complete with Norfolk jacket which many of the older generation will remember with nostalgia. For many weeks now the hard work has been forging ahead at a furious pace, with costume fittings, hand finishing and decoration and now all reaching its final stages."

"Surely that's it"

"Finally, it is only someone like Miriam Sullivan-Cody who could take on such a task and when the curtain rises on "The Boy Friend" next Wednesday, London will have occasion to see for itself the full range of her mastery!"

"Wow" she said. "That's quite something to live up to."

"Shall I read it again?"

"No, no, once is quite enough" she said reaching for her coffee again.

"You know I could never have done this without you David. You have always looked after me through thick and thin especially through that Len business."

"If you must know, I thought he was ghastly to you."

"I know, but I simply could not have picked up the pieces without the distraction of the designer business."

She reached over the coffee table and put her hand over his. "Why do all the best people I know have to be gay?"

"Now you're flirting with me Miriam."

"I have to just bury myself in work. I can't afford to have my heart broken again."

"You would have made a good mum."

"Oh don't say that it makes my heart ache so much."

MARJORIE 1980s
LONDON

LIKE MANY MOTHERS to teenage daughters, Marjorie had found it difficult being a good mother to Rosie. She would always want what was best for her, and would wherever possible, not compromise her demands. Money was not an issue, as she had been left comfortably off, financially, after Arthur died. Now her daughter wanted to be in Central London. And they had just moved, for the fifth time to a flat in Maida Vale, close to Warwick Avenue tube station. The Wimbledon Semi Finals were playing on the small television in the corner. Marjorie started to slowly unpack the boxes that the removal men had left behind. Over the years they had acquired so much junk, that she felt she just couldn't get rid of, souvenirs from all the countries they had travelled to recently.

"I can't believe you bought this manky old sponge mum!" said Rosie.

"At least I haggled for it."

They were gradually unwrapping the various objects from the scrunched up newspaper. Rosie was pouring over some of the albums, Marjorie had put together. She had carefully recorded each year of Rosie's life in those albums. Rosie on the beach, Rosie at the swimming baths and Rosie on her first day of school standing proud in her new uniform. She was growing more and more into Miriam each day and that saddened Marjorie.

She had said to Rosie that she didn't mind if Rosie wanted to find her real mother. After all it was understandable. But she was slightly worried if she encouraged her too much, that she might lose Rosie. Miriam was beautiful and artistic and probably all the things that Rosie would often criticize Marjorie for not being.

"I just don't understand why we don't buy some new furniture, Mum, I mean these chairs are a bit dated. Don't you think we should buy some sofas?"

Rosie was lying out on the rug idly flipping through the pages. Marjorie was knelt down beside her riffling through the boxes.

If truth be known, Marjorie couldn't bear to let anything go of Arthur's. Each house, they had moved to was a shrine to him. All she had now was Rosie and even she was going to be leaving home soon, to go to boarding school. Marjorie had agreed to it because she knew it was what Rosie wanted. Marjorie didn't know how she was going to cope on her own.

"Remember that time we were in Morocco and you were so ill? I thought you were going to die!" said Rosie.

"I know, I'm sorry, I think someone must have given me just a bit too much to drink" Marjorie retorted.

"I remember how kind everyone was to me that day." Rosie replied wistfully, leaning on her elbow.

"I know we haven't always seen eye to eye, but you won't be too lonely when I've gone to boarding school, will you?"

"Oh no, I've got my charity work and besides, I thought I'd take up sculpting."

"Sculpting?" Rosie asked

"Yes, I've always fancied doing something creative. I was never good at art at school like you, but I think I can do something with these hands."

She slowly turned over her wrinkled palms. She wanted to make something before, it was too late. Her body was old but her mind was still trying to catch up. She still felt no older than when Arthur had died. She had watched Rosie grow from a child in to an adult. Where had all those years gone?

She got up and walked to the window. The sun was beating down outside on the grass below, turning a slight golden yellow. You could hear the quiet plop of the tennis balls on Centre Court, in the background.

"Bjorg wins the first set 6-4." ran the commentator on the television."

"Did you like boarding school mum?"

"Not really, love. I went when I was nine years of age. All my friends lived miles away, so I had quite a lonely upbringing."

Marjorie got up from the leather arm chair and picked up a bowl of strawberries from the table offering one to Rosie. She thought about all of those years at school when she hardly got to see her own parents.

"Rosie, you do know that you can contact your real mum if you want to?"

"Mum, we've been over this before, I don't want to, I mean I don't need to. If anything I am more intrigued about my father, having not had a father. I mean I bet I'm more like him."

Marjorie couldn't tell her daughter that she was the spitting image of Miriam. She knew that Rosie was soon to become an adult and would be flying the nest, but she didn't want to lose the connection they had albeit a tenuous one. But she couldn't help but accept she wasn't getting any younger herself. She didn't want to be one of those people that lived on and on. She didn't want to be a burden to anyone. Yet she still doubted her faith, even more so now that Rosie was leaving. She had thought of converting to Catholicism, but the thought of never seeing Arthur again tormented her.

Perhaps when Rosie left home she would find the answers she was looking for.

ROSIE 1980s
LONDON

B Y THE TIME Rosie was seventeen, her adoptive mother offered her the chance to go to boarding school and she grabbed the opportunity. Unlike most children, she wanted to leave home. She knew the school because they had been there for their summer holidays. It was a boy's school with stringent entry requirements for the girls, that she passed with flying colours. They put her down however, for the house with the clergymen's daughters.

They arrived on the first day for tea with the housemaster and his wife. The house was set in its' own grounds just outside the main school. The drawing room was neatly laid out with old antiques and sofas. About six other new girls were also there with their parents. Some of the older pupils were also there to greet them.

"So how do you think you will cope with boarding school my dear?" the wife asked Rosie handing her a cup of tea.

"Just fine." she replied surveying the normality around her, albeit a somewhat formal one. She couldn't say that anything was preferable to being at home. She was looking forward to carving out a life for herself, one that involved her on her own.

She settled into school life pretty quickly. It was in some respects easier than her previous school. Everybody formed friendships within the confines of the school. You were cool, not because of the possessions you had, but for your personality and looks. Many of the pupils were from very established backgrounds albeit some of them quite dysfunctional ones. Her favourite subject was art. She used to spend hours in the art room, drawing and painting life and still life art. It was a wonderful feeling to loose herself in the pieces she was creating.

She also started to concentrate on her other studies and would work late in the night to revise for her exams. The house she was in was cold at night and had no central heating. She would wake up in the night and creep in to the toilet to switch a light on and then light a cigarette, even though it was forbidden by the school rules. Smoking had become her new friend, the imaginary mother, she had never met.

"Why do you smoke?" She was often asked.

Because even though she was privileged and lucky to be given a good start in life, that something was not enough. She wanted to take away the pain of being adopted.

Music was her solace. She bought a new digital stereo from London and was allowed to put it in her study. It was the coolest stereo by far and she bought it with her earnings from a summer job with "Next" in London. She started to collect a range of music, from soul to rock. She remembered starting out with the Human League and Spandau Ballet and moving on to Imagination and Michael Jackson. She would often hear U2 blasting out "In the name of love" in the mornings from the various houses.

In the summer holidays, her adoptive mum got a job for her in the Old Bailey on a fraud trial. The building was awe inspiring and she realized that this was the place she wanted to be in when she was older, amongst the old wigs and books of learning. The Court was like a stage with every actor playing their part. She didn't think the jury understood a bit of evidence, and the judge had to keep interpreting the case for them.

She did so well in her exams, they asked her to do Oxbridge. She applied to a small college in Cambridge and was asked for an interview. She remembered taking the train to London and then changing at Liverpool Street. Her heart was pumping so fast. She had rehearsed her answers, and knew it would be a challenge. The train went chugging through the rolling countryside until it arrived at the beautiful city. The tall spires stretched in to the autumnal sky.

"Why Cambridge?" The interviewer asked her. "And why history?"

"Because in the summer holidays, I did some work experience in the Old Bailey and I think I might eventually want to do a career in Law."

"Do you have any past connections with the college?" He asked.

"Well my Uncle was here many years ago, but I would like to think I will be judged on my current merits." She replied.

After a grueling two hour interview she went back to the college house. When she got the offer, she realized that art was no longer to be her chosen career, but a legal one. She knuckled down for those exams. The wait for those results in the summer was unbearable.

"You haven't got the grades darling. I am sorry." Her adopted mum said.

"But that can't be." She said. "Can't we get them remarked?"

She made all the telephone calls, to the School, to the university. The only way forward was to take a year out and do the exams again. Cambridge had said they would keep the offer open.

Rosie was devastated. What was she to do now? She couldn't stay at home now. She wanted to get on with her life. But what was the point of going to university, if it was not Cambridge? Maybe she should go straight to Law School now and not do a degree? Was it too late to get a place? They put her on the milk round to see what other university would have her.

"They've got a place for you at Kent." Her adoptive mother said.

"Where the hell is that! I've never heard of it."

Her half brother came to see them, one of the sons from her father's previous marriage. He had now retired from a lucrative job in Abu Dhabi.

"Have you got anything better to do?" He asked

"No." She replied.

"Well I suggest you give it a try and if you don't like it, you can always move on to something else." He said.

She met her future husband to be at that university. They established that they had both been in Puerto Banus and Sotogrande at the same time where his father kept a boat. After a few dates, he asked if she wanted to go back to his family home at the weekend. His friends said that his family were really nice and that she should meet them. She was nervous because she hadn't told him she was adopted and she didn't want to introduce him to her mother for fear of losing him. The moment he meets my mother and our set up, he won't like me, she thought.

They drove down in his car to his parents in the Midlands. Nothing prepared her for his family's house which was a beautiful Georgian house in the country or his family who were young and vibrant and liked the finer things in life. They had a great weekend, shooting and drinking and meeting his friends at the local pub. Rosie was absolutely dreading the drive back to London. They sat in silence on the way back, listening to the music on the radio. The roads were pitch black, the lights of the passing cars mesmerising them. As they approached Paddington, he asked.

"Whereabouts do you live? You will have to give me directions."

"Oh you can just drop me off in Clifton Gardens."

"I can't just drop you off in the vicinity. It's dark and anyway, I'd like to meet your mother."

No you wouldn't, she thought, or see my flat, or the furniture and how dated everything was.

"I haven't told her you are coming." She replied.

"Well, it will be a nice surprise then."

Oh no, she thought. How can he think that this is her mother when he meets her? Will he ever want to see her again? And they had had such a perfect weekend. His father was gregarious, his mother beautiful and his sisters were lovely. They had nice things, good dress sense. They had fun. How would he view her imperfect world, or anyone for that matter? She had not brought anyone to meet her mum. Surely he would leave her? They parked up outside the mansion block and took the rickety lift up to the fifth floor apartment. She had explained over the intercom that she had brought someone to see her. After making the necessary introductions, she offered them a drink and they sat awkwardly round the table. It was all very formal for what was meant to be an impromptu get together. After an hour he left.

"I'll see you back at Uni, when we get back the week after next."

And with that she closed the door, not knowing if she would see him again. He didn't phone, but that wasn't unusual for him. However, by now she was pretty sure she had found her soul mate and she didn't want to lose him.

When she got back to university, she needn't have worried. They still kept seeing each other and the relationship got more serious. Then one day out of the blue they bumped in to each other outside lectures.

"I'm glad I bumped in to you, something's wrong." She said.

"What do you mean?" He asked.

"I think I might be pregnant." She said. The words just hung in the frosty wintry air between them. He gave her a cuddle and stroked her hair. Then he spoke again.

"I don't mean to be insensitive, but I thought you were on the pill?" he said, looking at her straight between the eyes.

"I was, I mean I used to, but stopped before I came to University. I didn't think I would meet someone straight away, like you. But I simply can't have an abortion. I've never told anyone this before, but I am adopted. My adoptive mother couldn't have her own children because she was too old, so she adopted me. She would never agree to an abortion because she is totally against it. I'm really scared."

Then she told him about what she knew about her real parents, about the story of her adoption, everything that her mother had said to her in her letter to her. She poured her heart out like she'd never poured it out before. She told him she was too frightened to admit to people that she was adopted. Then he asked.

"Why don't you try and contact your real parents? I could help you."

"Because it would kill my adoptive mother. I don't know, she is old now and who knows? I know it sounds awful, but maybe, I just wait until she is gone and then I try and contact her?"

Having met her adoptive mother he was inclined to agree. They made an appointment to see the doctor on campus. She was a nice Chinese lady, who sympathized with their plight. Luckily she had had a false alarm. Despite the trauma of the day, she felt an immense relief at finally telling someone about her demise. She felt a huge weight lifted off her shoulders. It was bad enough being adopted, let alone, not admitting as such.

From then on they had a connection. They should have been studying but it was his last year at University whereas it was her first, so she could do the catching up with her studies later.

She didn't have any accommodation at the time so they moved in together into a tiny box room on campus. They crammed their studies in when they had to. Then if the sun was shinning they would drive off to Margate and play in the arcades. They even joined the local Casino. They loved those times in the dark, playing the roulette tables, hearing the ball as it dropped and rolled around the wheel. They spent many days losing and winning. They knew it was dangerous, but the thrill of winning became an obsession.

About that time, she inherited some money from her uncle. She needed it as her grant money was running out. She had always wanted a nice car. Anything but a clapped out mini. She hadn't passed her driving test. She persuaded the family lawyer to sell some shares and buy a car. She never drove the thing. It just sat outside their house, their box room. Like the stereo she had bought, it was something modern, something new, something to be proud of.

As the year drew to a close, She knew that they were going to be parted as it was his last year at university. He was looking for a job as an accountant in the City, so she knew they wouldn't be far apart, but still, she was going to need to pass her driving licence, if she had any hope of seeing him again. Luckily she passed it that summer and sold her car to buy his old car, which was a more sensible purchase. The first time she drove it down the motorway was in October 1987, the day after the storm to see him.

She had been to one of the college bars the night before and went to bed about midnight. She slept like a log that night as she usually did and awoke the following morning desperate for some orange juice. She jumped in the car and made for the nearest garage. As she drove along she noticed a tree across the road and drove round it. She drove round another one and another one. By the time she got to the garage, she must have mounted the pavement seven times. She realized a catastrophe had happened, when she saw a tree smashed through four vehicles, the fourth one left unscathed. They couldn't get any television so she went to a friend's house to listen to what was going on. The M2 was closed and she wanted to know when it was going to open, so that she could drive to London.

"We are just receiving news that the entire country is paralysed as a result of the worst storms this century." It said on Invicta Radio.

"Rosie, if the motorway opens, are you able to give me and Glen a lift to London?" one of her friends asked.

"I don't know. You might find it a bit hairy. It will be the first time that I have driven down the motorway, but you can come if you want to."

They waited for hours for the motorway to open to make the most difficult drive to London in her life. The winds were still 90 miles an hour and it was raining heavily. The guys who came with her had the music of Soul to Soul "Back to Life" on flat out. Every lorry she passed, she had to close her eyes as she thought they were going to topple over.

"Don't worry Rosie," they shouted. "You missed that one."

She arrived in Pimlico a nervous wreck. The journey had taken them four hours, when it should have taken them an hour and a half. They met in the pub and quickly downed two pints.

"Where to now?"

"Let's go to Stringfellows or the Hippodrome. I've got membership."

They all rolled into a black cab and headed for the West End. The night club was heaving. There were large screens playing the latest music videos. They drank cocktails on the top floor, served by bunny ladies. Then they danced the night away on the dance floor. The lights, the music, all the epitome of the eighties. These were one of the many nights they enjoyed clubbing in London. There was a lot of money sloshing around at the time. Every cocktail bar was heaving with city boys eager to spend their bonuses.

At the end of the evening they would grab a Chinese or a kebab and walk along the Piccadilly, through Green Park to his apartment in Pimlico. It was only tiny, but it was his. On Monday morning he would have to go to work and she would have to go back to university.

By Christmas 1987, her "Husband to be" had to move back to the Midlands to start a business with his father. In retrospect he should have finished his training in London, but his father was a persuasive figure and had been successful before in what he did. She was now fighting for his son's attention. She could remember when he was called back for his 21st birthday. His birthday was so close to Christmas, she couldn't be with him. That hurt and the fact that they were going to enjoy a big family Christmas. Christmas was always a lonely affair at her mother's. He had been promised so much for his 21st, that he ran back to his family. Those promises as it turned out were broken as was the idyllic family life that she was so envious of.

MIRIAM 1988
IRELAND

Cherish every moment
Life is too short
Don't waste a minute
Enjoy each day
And everyone in it
Tomorrow will come
It could be your last
Make the most of today
Life passes too fast
Annonymous

I T WAS THE "After Show" party. They had had the best night
of their lives, showcasing the latest designs her label had seen on
television. The music was pounding, the models had been strutting
their lean bodies on the catwalks. Miriam was so proud of the team
that evening. They had been instrumental in pulling everything
together. The atmosphere was electric.

"Miriam the designs were fabulous!"

"When's your next collection?"

She was bathing in the warmth of their praise that evening. As the models started to undress and pack behind stage, she edged towards her sister, Orla, who was barking out instructions to the girls to tidy away the props and get everything sorted for the next launch.

"Well done sis, we did it"

"No, you did it Miriam, the designs were fantastic!"

David popped open a bottle of Champagne and they held out their glasses, as he poured the sweet fizzy liquid into their glasses.

"Well done girls," he exclaimed. "I knew you could do it."

David ushered them over to the sofas which were covered in magazines and flowers, a testament to their latest success. The music started to blare from the speakers with music from Simply Red "Money's too tight to mention"

"So." David said "Money isn't too tight to mention now!"

"No." Miriam responded, frightened to acknowledge her own success, but what a success it had been. Some of the reviews in the latest magazines had likened her designs to John Rocha. The order book was relentless for the latest collection. Soon they would need to expand.

They allowed David to waft off in the direction of his gay companions who had supported them throughout their campaign. They felt like family to them now.

"We don't want to spoil his fun." Miriam said.

Her sister slowly nursed her flute of champagne and then asked her directly.

"Sis, if I didn't know you better, I would think you are hiding something."

For whatever reason, Miriam momentarily lost grip of her champagne flute and it smashed to the floor. A few people looked round slightly perplexed, but she couldn't return their gaze. She didn't want to ruin the rave reviews they were going to get the following morning. Her eyes started to well up with tears.

"Sis, whatever is the matter! You can tell me you know."

"Not here."

"Well how about I take you outside?"

They edged outside of the venue, specifically hired for them by David, a large Warehouse in Dublin.

"Not through there sis, the Press will find us."

So Orla found a small emergency exit, out towards the River Liffey and they sat down on a wall overlooking the Dublin City lights reflecting on the water.

"I found a lump, on my breast today."

"What do you mean?"

"A huge one, there is no mistaking it. It is pressing against my chest all the time and is excruciatingly painful. Here touch this."

She guided her sister's hand to her breast.

"Have you seen a doctor?"

"Not yet, but after our family history, I don't hold out much hope, do you?"

"Sis, stop this, they have amazing cures nowadays. You're only 43. Here have a cigarette, not that I should be offering you one."

Miriam gladly took it and Orla lit it for her. She could hear the bass of the music behind them, whilst the fog descended on the river. Every intake of the cigarette she took would produce willows of smoke into the night air.

"You know, I've known for some time sis."

"Why didn't you get it checked out?"

"Because I thought it would go away, not get bigger."

"Why do you feel the need to keep everything so bastard secret! I thought you'd learnt your lesson on that one Miriam."

"Maybe that's it. Maybe that is why I have the cancer, as punishment?"

"You don't know it's cancer yet sis. Let's get it checked out first."

The following day Miriam went to see an Oncologist in Dublin. They took various CT and PET scans, wheeled her in and out for various blood tests and took her blood pressure. Every test was more invasive, every test closer to the inevitable diagnosis. Finally she got to see Doctor Farmer.

"Miriam, I'm afraid I haven't got any good news. You have an aggressive cancer in your left breast, which I fear has spread to your lymph system. Had you come to us sooner, I might have been able to treat you, but the fact it has spread to your lymph system means, even if I start chemotherapy on your breasts your immune system is ultimately going to let you down."

"What are you saying doctor?"

"I'm saying that you are going to be in a lot of pain for some time, with no sight of recovery."

"You mean there's no cure?"

"Not yet."

"Will I have to go into a hospice?"

"No I don't see a need for that, but you will need heavy duty medication and I'm afraid your left arm will start failing you."

"But I need my arms for fashion designing."

"Miriam, this is not a time to carry on working. I suspect the stress of your job has probably brought on this cancer more aggressively. You need to slow down."

Outside her sister was waiting. She handed her a warm cup of tea with lots of sugar in it.

"What's the prognosis?"

"Not good sis. I'm dying of cancer."

And with that they hugged each other for a very long time.

"What now?"

"You need to rest."

"Will I ever find Rosie?"

"I don't know, but let us hope to God she finds you."

Cancer is like a weed, it grows faster than the flowers. Miriam could pretty much face things head on, running, but this disease was defeating her. All the chemo in the world wasn't going to help her on this one. She had achieved so much in a short space of time, and now it was being taken away from her. It was just a shame that she couldn't impart some of that success to Rosie. She had tried contacting Marjorie at the last known address, but she had moved. She couldn't blame her. The last thing she wanted, was Miriam harassing her, yet part of her thought that she might establish contact some time, but she never did.

She had hoped that by becoming relatively famous, that her daughter would have noticed her somehow and tried to make contact herself. Maybe she blamed her for giving her up? Who wouldn't? And now she had cancer. Was this her punishment? Was this where she had gone wrong in life, giving up her baby for adoption?

No amount of explanations could stop the avalanche that was descending on her now. All she could hope for, were that the memories she left behind would be enough for her daughter to cling on to if she ever found her. Realities fade but memories are eternal for those they leave behind. Her love for Rosie never faltered, she would just never have time to find out in her lifetime.

She went to see Father Amon at the local St Paul's Church in Macroom. It was time to make her confession. The church was serenely quiet when she entered. The wooden pews were lined side by side before the altar. She made her way to the confessional box in the far left corner. Sunlight was streaming through the stained glassed windows, illuminating the gold cross on the altar. She slowly pulled back the red velvet curtain and sat in the cubicle.

"Yes my child?" the Father said

She clung on to her rosary and fiddled nervously with the beads.

"Forgive me Father, for I have sinned."

"What is it my child?"

"Years ago, when I was 23 years of age, I had a relationship with a man out of wedlock. I believed it was true love, and although I know it was against the will of the Catholic Church, I bore his child."

"Go on"

"I couldn't go through with an abortion, so forgive me Father, I gave my baby away. Ever since, I've found it impossible to live with this lie, with myself and my family. And now I have found out I am dying of cancer and all I can think of is that God is punishing me in some way."

"God works in mysterious ways, my child, but he does not condemn us to death. He commits all those who believe, into eternal life. That is why Jesus was condemned for us."

"I feel like the devil incarnate, for giving away a life."

"My child, whatever the Catholic Church may have thought of at the time, you did not give away a life, you gave a child a life, to a family, that would have made her, I'm sure, very happy. You did not abort this child as you could have. Out of love for her, you gave her life and love."

"But however much I love her, I'm dying now and know that I'll never be able to see her."

"A lot can be achieved through the power of prayer. Let us join in the prayer of forgiveness."

And with that they said the Lord's Prayer.

Our Father, who art in Heaven
Hallowed be thy name
Thy kingdom come
Thy will be done
Now as it is in Heaven
Give us this day our daily bread
And forgive us our trespasses
As we forgive those who trespass against us
And lead us not in to temptation
But deliver us from evil
For thine is the kingdom the power and the glory
Forever and ever

Amen

"I can't say that God can save you from cancer, but he can restore your soul Miriam. Your belief will be stronger than your being."

As she left the Church, she tugged her coat around her and walked amongst the grave stones. She didn't want to be buried here amongst the dead. She wanted to be scattered in the ocean in to the Sea of Life. The Catholic Church, had been her enemy, when Rosie was born, forcing her to keep secrets, that she should never have kept. Now she needed the Catholic Church more than ever. She was truly scared now. What was death like? And would she be reunited with her loved ones in the after life? At least she knew she was dying, that life wasn't suddenly being taken away from her. All she knew was life was fragile, it could be taken away in a heart beat.

Cork Examiner February 1988

"Death of Top Fashion Designer"

"One of the Country's top fashion designers, Miss Sullivan-Cody of 3a Woods Place, York Street Cork, has died after a long illness.

A daughter of Mrs Bridget Sullivan-Cody and the late Charles Sullivan-Cody, she graduated from St Martin's Academy of Fashion Design in London, and returned to her native Cork where she opened her own couture business. Miss Sullivan-Cody's designs of evening, cocktail and daywear soon became nationally known and her splendid work was to be found in the Nation's top boutiques. Her evening gowns were featured in the Late Late Show's fashion spectacular. Miss Sullivan-Cody whose father was a former editor of the hoteliers magazine Mine Host, is survived by her mother, her sister Orla and brothers Frederic and Matthew.

Miriam 1988 – Ireland

A million times we've needed you. A million times we've cried

If love alone could've saved you. You never would have died

In life we loved you dearly. In death we love you still

In our hearts you hold a place. No one else will ever fill

It broke our hearts to lose you. But you didn't go alone

Part of us went with you. The day the Angels took you home

Annonymous

ROSIE 1989–96
LONDON

WHEN YOU ARE adopted you have this profound need for love and profound fear of rejection. It's not that you lack love, it's just that you don't have that genetic love that is bestowed on everyone else around you. People love you for you, but you don't know who "you" is? Often people say there is something special about you, but you don't feel special inside. You feel that life let you down in some way, that two people that loved once didn't love you. They brought you into the world, then cast you off to make you find your own way in life like a kitten or puppy. Rosie often looked at dogs, and thought poor things, you were once put up as puppies for sale, forever taken away from your mother. That was what happened to her. She was placed in a loving home, albeit a dysfunctional one, but she was never to know the true meaning of love with her real mother, even if she did set out to find her.

Nothing was to become so apparent, when after seeing her "husband to be" for the entire period of university and beyond law school, she had finished her exams. She had put all her heart into her finals, as she realized this was her only ticket to freedom and a professional life, one that would give her the independence, she craved. They had just got back from a weeks holiday in Italy. They were sitting in a pub in Godalming in Surrey. She was excited about her future, their future together. She was due to start a job in London in September. The world was her oyster. Her adoptive mother was due to go on holiday to Canada for a month, to meet all her friends from the post war era. All she had to look after, all she was responsible for, was the cat in London.

"I can't wait to come up and stay with you in Worcester." She said.

"You're not coming."

"What do you mean I'm not coming."

"It's over."

"What do mean it's over?!"

"I can't do this anymore."

Tears were streaming down her face. Everything she had worked so hard for, was now imploding. Her rock, the one person she had relied on during her emotional journey was letting her down. One of the things she had learnt about the insecurity of adoption, is never to let your guard down, no matter how much it hurts.

"You do realize, that if you say it's over, I don't do friends. I mean this means, we will never see each other again."

Like the mother that had abandoned her she felt abandoned.

There were hugs and kisses in the car park, an inevitability, that they would never see each other again. She was in London, he was in Worcester. Their paths would not be crossing. As they drove up the A3, in their separate cars, his car took the turning on the M25 to the Midlands, hers to London. When she got back to the flat in Little Venice on her own, she just locked herself away, back in the crazy existence of her adoptive mother's flat without her adoptive mother. She had no one to cling on to now, no one to give her the comfort she craved. She didn't know who she was or who she was to become.

Over the next few days it was probably one of the most difficult and cathartic experiences. The ability to find out finally who she was. She poured over old letters and diaries, trying to make sense of herself. She had come to rely on someone else too emotionally, and they had let her down, just as her real mother had let her down. The only person she had now was her adoptive mother, but she wasn't there to carry the pieces. But it wasn't her that she needed, it was her that she was trying to get away from. She needed to find herself. No one else could do that for her now. Not even her real mother.

At least she had the flat to herself, but it was such a depressing place. Everywhere she looked was a shrine to her father. The same battered armchairs and furniture never to be updated. Life was for living, not dying. She knew she needed to get rid of the shackles of death. Why be so depressed when there was so much to live for?

One day she grabbed her car keys and decided to drive round the streets of South Kensington. She'd lost all touch with her mates since she'd been in this relationship, it was time to go and find them. She drove round and round behind the old streets off Kensington High Street until she finally found a group of her friends standing outside Abbey Mansions.

"Oh my God! I am so glad I've found you guys. I have been almost suicidal. I haven't seen anyone in days"

"Come and join us for a drink at the The Sporting Page. All the usual crew are going to be there. We've missed you."

"Why don't some of you jump in. I"ll give you a lift."

Over the following weeks, she managed to pick up the pieces and started going out and meeting people. She slowly regained confidence and realized how people all around her actually liked her. She miraculously bumped into some of her "Husband to be's" friends in London. She knew the message would get back to him in Worcester.

Eventually her "husband to be" called and asked.

"Would you like to come on holiday to Scotland with me?"

"Why would I want to do that, when last time I went on holiday with you, you sacked me?"

He laughed.

"I'd better come down to London and persuade you then."

They got married a few years later.

Rosie fondly remembered when they found out they were pregnant with their first child. They were on their way to Edinburgh with her parents in law for her sister in law's twenty first birthday. They planned to stop on the way in Lake Windermere, to stay in an expensive hotel which her father in law huffed and puffed about the price of. They chartered a yacht on Lake Windermere and sailed on the lake on a cold summer's day. Then they walked the hills. She often looks at the photographs of that day and stares in wonderment that she was actually pregnant in those photos, although she didn't know it then. They were to find out when they were in Edinburgh.

They checked in to a smart town house hotel, close to the centre. As they were unpacking their suitcases, she said to her husband

"I think I might be pregnant."

"How long have you suspected?"

"I don't know but I don't feel sick or anything."

"Lets go for a walk and go to the chemist. We can catch up with my parents later."

They grabbed their coats and started to walk the streets of Edinburgh. The city was Georgian in stature, overshadowed by the castle on the hill. They popped in to the chemist on the way and picked up a pregnancy test. They then went in search of a local pub.

"You sit down in the corner, I'll get the drinks."

Her husband went to the bar and got a pint of bitter for himself and a glass of white wine for Rosie.

"Are you going to do the test now?"

"I can't do the test in the pub toilet!" She exclaimed.

They were both dying to know. They hadn't been trying for a baby for very long, so the news that she might be pregnant was a bit of a shock. She'd never taken a pregnancy test before, even though she thought she might be pregnant at university but wasn't. She took out the packet and read the instructions. Her husband's parents were not getting on well at the time and were only showing solidarity for the sake of their daughter's birthday. The short break in Lake Windermere had done little to appease the situation.

When they got back to the hotel room, she ventured to the toilet and shut the door. The instructions were quite clear, if a blue line came up on the tester, she was pregnant. She took the test.

"Oh my God, I'm pregnant!" She exclaimed excitedly.

"Are you sure? I bought another pregnancy test, just in case."

She took another test and another clear blue line appeared.

"I'm definitely pregnant."

They hugged each other for some time, letting the reality of their wonderful creation set in. They were also, if they were honest a little bit daunted. What did pregnancy entail? None of her friends had been pregnant yet. She didn't have a mother to explain what pregnancy and birth entailed, only motherhood.

"We can't tell anyone tonight. I don't want to ruin your sister's birthday. Anyway I want a drink and if I announce I'm pregnant then everyone will expect me to stop drinking and smoking and I am not quite ready to do that just yet."

They got together that evening, safely guarding their new found secret. They wanted to tell the whole world, but didn't want to take the wind out of her sister in law's sails. How different her elation was to that of her real mother's devastation, twenty nine years before. How she still ached to find her. Yet her adoptive mother was still going strong.

The following day they were driving back down the motorway, all four of them in silence. They were gearing up the courage to tell her parents in law the news.

"We've got something to tell you. You are about to be grandparents."

"That's great news," they both chorused.

"Let's stop off at the next service station and have a celebratory lunch."

They sat quietly in that service station, mulling over the truck stop fare.

"I'm not sure I'm ready to be a grandparent."

"I wonder if it is a boy or a girl?" her father in law pondered.

Rosie and her husband knew that men always secretly wanted a boy. Perhaps that's why her father didn't want her. Maybe he would have wanted her more, if she had been a boy? On the journey back, all they could talk about was the names for it if it was a boy or a girl.

For Rosie, pregnancy was like throwing a duck to water. She had no morning sickness and pretty much carried on as normal. She still wasn't showing when she had her first scan.

"Baby and mum are doing just fine," the nurse said, patting her arm.

"I hope you will attend some of the antenatal classes we offer?"

In truth, she could not be bothered with these classes. Everybody got pregnant and gave birth. Surely there was nothing to it? She bought a book on pregnancy which showed and explained the various stages of pregnancy. As the months went by, She slowly began to feel the baby move and kicking inside her. One night she woke up in the middle of the night and saw a whole limb moving. She nudged her husband and they stared in awe at this little creature. Their baby was turning around like some alien.

Towards the end of the pregnancy, she began to feel uncomfortable. She could see how her mother had managed to conceal her pregnancy, pretty much until the end, because she hadn't eaten for two, she didn't show until the last month or so.

On the morning of the 9th January 1996, two weeks earlier than predicted, she awoke at 6 am to find her waters had broken. Whilst her husband was scrabbling around for the book, finding out what to do, she ran a bath. Her husband telephoned the midwife.

"How long between her contractions?"

"I don't know."

"Just stay and rest at home and ring us again, when the contractions begin."

As she was running the bath, she could feel the contractions coming every ten minutes or so. They were excruciatingly painful when they came, giving her little reprieve.

"Forget the bath, I'm taking you to the hospital."

She had to step gingerly across the black ice to get to the car. She couldn't get in at first as she was in yet another contraction. As they set off, she wound down the window and hastily lit another cigarette.

"I don't know if I can make it to the hospital." she said, when they arrived in the hospital car park.

"Just wait until the contraction passes and then we will leg it to the maternity unit." Her husband replied.

They were ushered straight in to the labour ward, which seemed surprisingly quiet at 7 o' clock in the morning. There appeared to be only one midwife on the ward.

"I can't take the pain any more. Get me some pain killers now!" She cried out.

"Just stay there. Someone will be with you shortly. Just breathe in gas and air."

She couldn't stay still. The contractions were now coming quick and fast, like a ton of bricks on her spinal cord.

"Just take away the pain!" She cried.

Ten minutes later the midwife came back.

"I'm afraid it is too late for an epidural. The baby is coming, just push!"

For the next ten minutes, she screamed and cried and shouted as her little baby came in to the world. It felt like every muscle was being torn. Her husband was now on the gas and air.

"Congratulations, you have a baby boy!"

And with that she heard a little cry and whilst they cut the cord and cleaned him up she looked straight in to her husband's eyes. For Rosie, it felt truly miraculous, that feeling of giving birth. From that moment their lives became insignificant. Death seemed less scary, because now, they truly had something to leave behind. The nurse gave her, her baby boy to hold in her arms, the tiniest, smallest being with his eyes closed. She checked to see that he had all his fingers and toes. At that very moment he looked all wrinkly, like an old man, but he was hers and he was beautiful.

The nurse wheeled her down to the ward with her baby, in a little cot beside her with a plastic tab on his ankle. No name yet, that was for later. That day, she was exhausted, exhausted with the physical effort and the emotion. She couldn't sleep for all the other babies crying. Her baby in contrast was beautifully silent, having just been born in to the world. That night, one of the nurses placed him next to her in bed and she just kept staring at him. How could her mother have given her away, she thought? It was nice to see him at last. Since they had already been together for nine months, she felt she already knew him.

When they left the hospital the next day, they did so in a little panic. How did you do the car seat? What if he needed feeding? How did she bath him? They moved in to her parents in law for a couple of days as the house they were moving in to wasn't ready yet. That day whilst their baby was sleeping they watched a movie.

Not long afterwards, she went back to work with the help of a local nanny. One day, she was driving through the forest when she heard the George Michael song "Jesus to a child". She burst in to tears uncontrollably and had to pull the car over. The enormity of giving birth, just overcame her. The fact that her real mother had given her up and here was her child, her little boy that she could never dream of giving up, like Jesus to a child.

Over the following weeks, her adoptive mother came to see them. She was seventy five now and she was reluctant for her to hold her baby, for fear she might drop him. It was cruel, she realized and she knew she was being hesitant, but she wasn't very steady on her own feet, let alone on her own feet and with a baby. Her husband would often comment.

"How did she cope? I can't believe social services didn't intervene."

On one occasion, she did trip over and from then on she was hugely protective. She went on to give birth to two more healthy children.

MARJORIE 2000s
LONDON

MARJORIE WALKED SLOWLY round her flat on the top floor of a mansion block in Maida Vale. The carpet was worn and frayed and needed replacing. Many of the cupboard doors looked tired in the kitchen. Her body was getting old now, and she found it difficult to get round without a walking stick. She walked over to the old Georgian display cabinet and picked up a framed picture of her daughter and her three grandchildren. They were growing up so fast now. She must remember to top up their bank accounts when she next went to the bank.

She went back into her bedroom to check that her trunk was still locked. She kept forgetting things these days and was often confused. Rosie had suggested that Marjorie might want to move in with them but she had politely declined. She didn't want to be a burden on Rosie. Why was everyone making such a fuss? In any event her daughter and son in law both had busy careers and three children to bring up. She didn't want to be a contributor to the so called "sandwich effect".

The telephone rang and Marjorie staggered to answer it.

"Mum, it's me."

"Hello darling." She said, slightly out of breath.

"How are you?"

"I'm OK."

Marjorie could hear the exasperation in her daughter's voice. She knew she wasn't very quick at getting to the phone these days. Her hips were aching after two hip operations and her balance was not what it used to be. She had fallen over a few times, but had not thought to mention it. She didn't want to worry Rosie.

"I've got something important to tell you."

"What is it?"

"You know that we are looking to move and that we have decided to sell the businesses?"

"Yes."

"Well we've decided to emigrate to France."

Marjorie started chewing her lip, trying to take this all in. She had refused all invitations to go and live with Rosie, but moving to another country? How was she going to cope? She loved Paris when she was younger, but getting on a plane was still alien to her, if she were honest. They had been on a few holidays, but for her daughter to move so far away. Her mind was racing. She couldn't get her head around the facts.

"Listen, we still want you to come and live with us. Any property we buy, will have an apartment attached. We're moving to the South, so the weather will be much better for you."

Marjorie couldn't let on that being in her eighties, made such a decision monumental. A new country, a new language, a new everything. Her body was too tired for all of this. Yet she couldn't let on to this, for Rosie's sake. She didn't want to go on and on, but was also scared of dying.

"Have you told your husband's parents?"

"Well my husband hasn't been getting on with his father recently, but his mother knows."

"Where will the children go to school? I thought they loved their school here." Marjorie said with a slight panic in her voice.

"Oh they'll probably go to an International School."

"When are you thinking of going?"

"Soon. We haven't sorted out the fine details, but you must come out with us in the Easter holidays. We've rented somewhere in the interim."

"What about flights?"

"I'll arrange those. Just say you'll come?"

"I'll think about it."

And with that Marjorie put the phone down. All she wanted was what was best for her daughter and grandchildren. Her daughter arranged for her to fly to Nice with them. Marjorie found the effort of getting to the airport and on to the plane exhausting. Once she got to France she found the whole idea of moving there depressing. She was used to her flat in Maida Vale. She was used to living on her own. She didn't want to start being sociable now. She didn't have the energy.

"I know it's not what you want to hear, but I can't come and live with you. You have your life to live. I just feel that I keep going on and on."

Marjorie could see that her daughter was saddened by her decision.

"At the very least can't we get you a carer? I worry about you so much now. You're not getting any younger."

"No." She said with some finality.

Eventually Marjorie heard from Rosie they had found the perfect house they wanted in a Domaine overlooking the medieval village of Saint Paul. Rosie told Marjorie that her husband had also re established contact with his father who had been trying to trace them in the South of France. Marjorie knew from her experience with Arthur that you couldn't be over cautious and told Rosie to tell her husband to make amends even though he was still young at 59.

She was surprised the following week when they both popped in to see her

"Hi Marjorie, how are you?"

She ushered them in to her apartment and offered them each a glass of wine. The flat was looking a bit shabby now. She needed to remind Rosie to try and get a cleaner.

"I've invited Dad to spend Christmas with us at our house in Saint Paul. We've booked the Colombe d'Or for Christmas Eve."

"Isn't that the famous hotel that Rosie has mentioned with paintings donated from Chagall, Renoir and Matisse?" Marjorie said gulping her wine.

"Yes, nearly always fully booked."

His dad stood up and looked at the photos of his grandchildren in the silver frames on the side. They had all grown up since he last saw them. They talked awhile about the South of France and how the children were settling in. Eventually when they could see that Marjorie was drifting in and out of consciousness, they put a blanket over her and said their goodbyes.

That was the last time, Marjorie's son in law saw his dad. Tragedy struck that Christmas when the weekend before Rosie had the rest of the family over. It was Saturday morning when Marjorie received the phone call.

"Mum."

"What is it?"

"Roger died this morning of a massive heart attack."

"Oh no I'm so sorry darling."

"He was like the father I never had."

"I know."

"I feel so guilty for not having seen him. Now he will never get to see his grandchildren."

"Grief affects us in various ways." Marjorie said.

She was in a state of utter shock herself. This was like the re run of Arthur dying, all those feelings of guilt and anguish returning. Why not me? Why do all the best people get taken. She'd always warmed to Roger. He was a difficult fellow, but no one deserved this?

She could hear her daughter sobbing on the other end of the phone.

"They're saying that he took a lease on a flat in Nice, just down the road from us!"

"You must go through the grieving process. It takes a long time."

Arrangements were made for everyone to fly back for the funeral. Marjorie was to fly back to Nice with Rosie and her husband the following day so she could spend Christmas with them. Christmas was a solemn affair, with only Marjorie, her stepson and family in tow. Over the following days, Rosie would talk to Marjorie, about how to handle the grief. As a family, they would often go down to Juan les Pins to watch the sun set over the water.

"Mum, I had to clear out the flat in Nice the other day."

"That must have been grim darling."

"The thing is, I know it sounds strange but every time I get in to the lift since he's died the lift stops."

"I often found that when your dad died."

"I went through his apartment and in the kitchen, poking out from one of the overhanging cupboards was a copy of the New Testament. He never mentioned that he was a Church goer, but I found it comforting, that he found God before he died."

Marjorie didn't have the answers any more. She daren't tell Rosie, but she had been seeing more and more strange visions, back at her apartment. In truth she was a little scared. She was sure that there had been people rummaging through her apartment.

One evening she was so scared, she hobbled out of her apartment and down the five flights of stairs, nearly tripping over her nightie as she reached the front entrance. The night air was freezing when she emerged outside in to the main road beneath her. She aimlessly walked through the streets and into the roads. Many cars and taxis had to swerve away to avoid hitting her. Many were blasting their horns.

"Watch out lady, you nearly killed yourself!" said a young man walking in the opposite direction. He grabbed hold of her arm. Marjories's hair was dishevelled and her eyes were bloodshot.

"Where am I?" she asked.

"You shouldn't be out here in your night clothes. You will catch your death!"

"I heard voices in my apartment."

The man held on to Marjorie as he retrieved his mobile and started typing in the numbers.

"I'm calling an ambulance." He said.

Back in France, Rosie was sitting on her terrace overlooking the medieval village of Saint Paul. She could see the moon shimmering on the Mediterranean sea in the distance.

"I'm a bit worried," she said to he husband whilst sipping a cool glass of wine and taking the first drag of her cigarette. They had just put the children to bed after a long day at school. They were now soaking up the evening air in their garden.

"I've rung my mother four times now and she has not answered. She shouldn't really be going out on her own with her walking stick. She could get mugged or anything could happen."

"I suggest you call the police first, see if they know anything."

Rosie called Paddington Green Police Station. She explained that she lived in France and was worried about her mother who was 82. They said they would make enquiries and get back to her. They did not call back for about an hour and Rosie was frantic with worry. Eventually they called.

"We have found your mother. She was walking the streets of London in her nightie. She thinks there were people in her apartment. They have admitted her to St Mary's Paddington. She has had a stroke."

Rosie did not know if it was the shock of the death of her father in law which caused the stroke or what. Her husband said it was ironic that the last hours he had spent with his father had been with Rosie's adoptive mother. Her adoptive mother was the one that kept saying she wanted to die young.

Marjorie remained in St Mary's for the next few months, before returning to her flat in Maida Vale. She would only agree to a carer if it was one that was privately employed by her.

All Rosie could think about from then on, was turning forty soon and wondering when she was going to make steps to find her real mother.

FINDING MIRIAM 2007
SOUTH OF FRANCE

"**I** JUST CAN'T BELIEVE IT!" exclaimed her husband "We go to the Colombe D'Or where normally it is so difficult to get a table and bump in to two Irish people who think they may know your real mother."

"I know, I can't quite believe it myself." She said taking another sip of wine from her glass. "Did I tell you that I bought a new diary a few months back and by pure coincidence my birthday falls on Saint Rosalie's Day in the Catholic calendar. I know my adoptive mother was thinking of calling me Sarah and my real mother named me Michelle. I mean why Saint Paul? We moved here by pure coincidence."

"I know." Her husband replied. "It feels like there is some religious significance to all this which is baffling."

The following week passed and there was no phone call relating to her birth mother. She began to despair that the whole thing had been a useless exercise and that the only way she was going to find her was by hiring a private detective, something she was loathe to do. She had for once been given hope that in some way her mother had found her, that she had not betrayed her adoptive mother in any way. Her husband always said that he thought someone was always looking out for her. She always seemed to possess a bit of luck in anything she turned her hand to. She was usually the eternal optimist and he was the eternal pessimist. However on this occasion she was beginning to despair as to what optimism was.

The weekend after that they were due to go out for a big weekend with her husband's sisters and their other halves at the Eden Roc in Cap d'Antibes. They decided not to go out for lunch that day as they were going for a big night out. She had a glass of wine at home and then decided to go to bed on the basis she didn't feel well. She was saddened by the fact they had received no phone call. To have hope and have that hope taken away is worse than no hope at all. She slipped in and out of consciousness that afternoon on their bed.

Suddenly the door burst open and her husband strode in.

"I've just been listening to the messages on my phone and there was one from Fidelma a week ago asking you to phone her back. Here take a listen."

Why had she doubted her? She took the phone and pressed the message button.

"Hi Rosie, it's Fidelma. I've got some news about your mother. Can you give me a call."

She knew from the tone of her message that something wasn't right. She took out her card and then took the portable out in to the garden to make the call.

"Hi Fidelma. How are you?"

"I'm fine thanks. Listen I've got some good news and bad news. The good news is that we found your mother, but she died of breast cancer at the age of 45. She was a famous model and fashion designer in Dublin and my mother used to buy her designs and became good friends with her. We have managed to find her only surviving sister who lives in Spain. Listen I know it is a long shot, but would you like to come to my daughter's christening in Macroom next weekend? I can sort out the hotels and a babysitter. We could arrange to meet some of your mother's best friends. There are direct flights I think from Nice to Cork every day. Please say you will come. We are all in shock here."

Tears poured down her face. She had found her mother too late. And yet, here was a chance to find out more about her, maybe go to Spain to see her sister. They hardly knew this couple, but Fidelma was being so kind.

"Of course we'd love to come. I'll check out the flights and call you back."

And then she put the phone down and howled with crying. Her husband held her tight. Even if she had gone in search of her would she have found her in time? How come she had found her in Saint Paul?

"We don't have to go out this evening you know. I can call my sister and cancel if you want to."

"No, don't cancel, I want to go. But don't dampen the evening by telling them the news. In some ways this is a small miracle this is happening. Let's enjoy this evening. We don't get to go out much these days without the children."

They booked the flights and she rang Fidelma to tell her they were coming that weekend. They told their eldest what was happening but not their other two. They didn't even know yet that she was adopted. They were still very young to digest this information. The babysitter arrived and they got changed. They then drove to the Eden Roc where they parked the car for them. They then met up with her husband's sisters and their partners on the terrace of the hotel for a glass of champagne. The terrace overlooked the gardens which stretched about a quarter of a mile down to the ocean. The light was beginning to fade as they sipped their cocktails.

"I can't believe the rooms here, they are amazing," said her husband's sister.

"They cost a small fortune." Said her partner. "Luckily the company are paying."

They were down there for a big PR party for various advertising companies in Cannes. Depending on how they all felt, the plan was to hit the VIP beach parties later on. They chatted to a few other people on the terraces who wanted to know where to go for lunch the next day. At about 8 o'clock they made their way down to the restaurant on the rocks overlooking the sea. The moon was shimmering on the water below. Their table overlooked the ocean where they could hear the waves crashing against the rocks below. It was such a beautiful setting. She squeezed her husband's hand. They both knew what she was thinking. She had found her mother, and next weekend who knew what the world would bring?

That evening they ate a very expensive meal and then piled in a convoy of taxis to go to the parties on the beach in Cannes. She managed not to say anything about the days' events until the end of the evening. Both her husband's sisters knew she was adopted but they hadn't really spoken much about it. Whilst they were recovering from the dancing on the sand with a cigarette in their hands she told them what had happened that day and that they were all going to Ireland the following weekend.

"I can't believe it. Rosie you will have to let us know what happens when you get back."

"The thing is, I still don't know what to expect. What will her friends be like, I wonder? Will they like me? Will I like them? And what about my father in all of this?

"You'll get the answers you are looking for. Ireland is meant to be a great place."

She was still in shock that night. She was looking forward to the forthcoming journey. It was what she had wanted all her life, to find out where she came from, where she belonged. But would she belong? Would the journey take her back to no man's land. One thing for sure she had her own family now in her husband's sisters and their three beautiful children.

ROSIE 2007
IRELAND

THE DAY BEFORE the planned trip for Ireland, they were busily packing their suitcases and getting their documents together. Their cleaner came to collect their dog. The children were excited about going on a mini holiday. Her husband checked the flights on the internet.

"Oh my God he said, I've booked the wrong dates. We're going to miss the christening."

"How did that happen?" She asked.

"I don't know I must have pressed the wrong button on the computer."

"We need to change them. What if all the flights are full? They are probably not transferable."

Her heart was pounding so fast, she broke out in a sweat. They couldn't not go to the christening. They just couldn't. Her husband frantically logged on to the internet.

"They've got five seats left. It is going to cost another five hundred euros. We don't have a choice."

After the longest thirty minutes ever they got their new tickets and reservations. They were booked on the 11 o' clock flight to

Cork on the Friday.

They queued at Nice airport Terminal One surrounded by Irish people. It felt very strange to hear the Irish accent. It had a lyrical quality to it. Once on the plane her husband settled down to playing cards with the boys. Rosie just sat and read with her daughter looking at the inflight magazine and reading up about Cork and the surrounding areas. The flight was only an hour and a half and when they landed it was raining. Everyone seemed very welcoming, in sharp contrast to France. They jumped in a hire car and headed off to Macroom. All the road signs were in Irish and English.

"Lets listen to some Irish music." The children sang along to the radio, as they left Cork behind them and set off for Macroom. The rain had stopped now and they started edging through the green countryside through small villages. Every now and then there would be an ancient ruin on the side of the road. There were also a number of new developments, the ones that Nick had referred to.

About half an hour later they reached Macroom, a small market town with a Castle in the middle. They were booked in to the Castle Hotel Macroom.

"Hello there, we're expecting you," beamed the receptionist. "We've sorted out a babysitter for you for 7 o' clock this evening. If you care for some lunch there's a restaurant on the ground floor open all day. I hope you enjoy your stay with us."

They took their bags up to their rooms and then went down to the restaurant. They were serving roast dinners, her husband's favourite.

"This gravy is wonderful, I thought yours was good."

"I wonder how they make it so good. Maybe there is an Irish secret to it."

That afternoon they walked around Macroom. There was a monument in the centre of the town dedicated to the IRA.

"You never know you may be related to them," her husband said. "This could explain a lot about you." he joked. From the monument they walked round the castle, and from there they walked up the high street to buy an antique silver bracelet for the christening. When Rosie spoke to the shop owner he confirmed that some famous films had been made in the area about the IRA, one including Liam Neeson. He wrote down on a piece of paper the names of those movies. She wanted to say that she was one of them, that she was Irish and that this was her home town. But she couldn't explain away her clipped English accent or the fact that she was in a small Irish town where she was yet to meet her mother's friends.

That evening they were getting ready for dinner. Fidelma had arranged for them to meet her first in the bar and then go to a little restaurant around the corner which served good food. She said that Nick was driving down from Dublin and would be joining them later. Rosie took great care that evening on what to wear. She put on some Joseph trousers with some high heels a small vest and a beautiful silk Armani jacket. Her hair was down and her make-up was perfectly applied. She wanted her mother's friends to like her and be proud of her.

They took the stairs down to the bar and Fidelma was waiting for them.

"Hello Rosie. You look nice this evening." She said blowing a kiss on both cheeks "How are you both?"

"Nervous." She replied.

"I know, I've never had to do anything like this before. I mean how weird that we met in the Colombe D'Or that day and that you mentioned your mother's name and that my mother knew her. If I could have called her at the restaurant I would have and put you out of your misery. Anyway you are here now."

"What will you have to drink?"

"Two gin and tonics. I'll get these." Her husband replied.

"The food here is really good, and the hotel seems really nice," she said.

"We're having the christening here tomorrow. We wanted it in our home town. It should be quite a knees up."

"Who are we going to meet tonight?"

"Well I have arranged for you to meet Humphrey and Pat who were great friends of your mother. They should have some photos and bits of memorabilia. They are well thought of in Macroom."

"I'm dying to meet them can we go now."

They left the bar and walked the short distance to a little fish restaurant. Rosie was nervous with anticipation, gingerly walking on her high heels over the cobbled pavement. When they got inside the restaurant was small and packed. They made their way to a table in the corner where a number of people were sat. All eyes were on Rosie. The restaurant was very noisy with people talking and laughing. Suddenly there was a hush. A woman with blonde hair and green eyes, the same as Rosie's, approached her. It was like looking at a spitting image of herself, as if looking in a mirror twenty years on.

"Hi I am your Aunty Orla."

Oh God she was her mother's sister, the one that was meant to be living in Spain. She was here, right here in this room. They both burst in to tears and hugged each other. Everyone cried.

"I thought you were in Spain."

"We were but we had to come back for a funeral."

They continued to stare at each other. Make up was streaming down their faces but they didn't care. This was the best present Rosie could have ever hoped for.

"This is my second husband Donald," she said.

"Hi."

"And these are your mum's friends Humphrey and Pat."

"Hi."

"I can't believe how like Miriam she looks," exclaimed Pat.

"I can't believe how like Orla she looks," exclaimed her husband.

Orla said there was so much she wanted to tell Rosie about her mother. She had, had so little time to put something together, but she had typed a resume in a little red folder with an original photograph of her as a Lucie Clayton model in the 1960's together with some other photos that Rosie could keep. She sat and turned the pages. The photo was the most beautiful photo she could have seen. She reminded her of her husband's mother. This would explain why her adoptive mother never got on with her husband's mother. She reminded her of her eldest. She slowly began to read the contents of the folder.

"Dear Rosie

I am going to meet you tonight for the first time in 40 years, the last time I saw you, you were a little baby. Miriam had called you Michelle and sadly gave you up for adoption and you were renamed Rosie.

A few years later, as far as I remember Miriam heard from your adoptive Mother, to say that your adoptive father had died. Miriam was very tempted to try and claim you back, but didn't want to break your mother's heart.

When Miriam put you up for adoption, she was not the success she became later in life. She often talked about you over the years, but when she got ill from cancer she talked about you a lot, and wondered how you were doing. Sadly I had no way of getting in touch with you.

I attach a brief story of Miriam and her family and some photos and articles that appeared when she established herself as a designer, manufacturer.

I hope the attached help to fill in the blanks in some way.

Orla

Miriam was born on the 20th May 1942, and grew up in a terrace house in an area still affectionately called Jew Town. At the time a lot of the neighbours were Jewish, Goldwaters, Goldbergs, Levin, Cohen etc, etc. The Sullivan-Cody's were a different family as well. Your grandmother a Catholic Corkonian, Bridget Barlow came from Blackrock in Cork. Your Grandfather a Londoner Charles John Sullivan-Cody from St Martins Lane, in the heart of London was brought up as a Baptist but later became a Catholic. He came to Ireland and was the publisher of a hotel magazine.

Rosie 2007 – Ireland

There were five of us, Frederic, Matthew, Miriam, Orla and James. Tragically James died in a car accident aged 31, then your grandfather died aged 88, he was 25 years older than your grandmother. Miriam sadly died in February 1988 and your grandmother died in December 1988. Matthew died in 1999 and Frederic sadly passed away last year. I am the only remaining member of the family.

Frederic had a son Mark

Matthew has a daughter April

Miriam one daughter Michelle (Rosie)

Orla one daughter Charlotte

James one daughter Orla and one son Charles

Miriam from an early age was very artistic and went to study Art at Cork School of Art (Crawford Gallery)

She went to London in the early 60's and passed out as a model at the Lucie Clayton School of Modelling. She decided not to pursue that career, instead went for a Designing Course at St Martins Lane Art College.

She also worked in London in Selfridges, went to work on a cruise ship etc, before finally returning to Ireland, where she started working in the rag trade. In the mid 1960's Miriam went to Dublin and started firstly working in Brown Thomas and then private dress designing dress making. It was during this time she met whom I believe was your father Len Jackson. I'm sorry I know very little about him, except he had lived a lot in South Africa and came back to Ireland. Miriam was madly in love with him.

I was living in North London at the time with my daughter Charlotte who was only a baby when Miriam came over as she was expecting you. You were born in either July or August I can't remember. Miriam sadly had to give you up for adoption, as she had no future with your father, and she thought it would be best.

It was after this that she started on her dress designing and things went on from there.

Your Mother was a beautiful woman. She was very talented and gifted and if she had lived she would have been the top Irish designer, ahead of John Rocha and everyone.

She was a very popular woman with her huge circle of friends in Cork. She was a fantastic sister. She had a wicked sense of humour, she was very good to her parents Mum and Dad, she was a great Aunty to my daughter Charlotte, she helped rear her. She was very witty, could be very caustic also, took no prisoners, told it as it was. She always gave out advice and sorted us all out.

I think she always regretted giving you up for adoption, as when the stigma had lifted about being a single parent, she was in a position to have given you a good home. I can only hope for Miriam's sake that your adoptive Mother was a good kind and caring woman."

Once Rosie had read this she started to flick through the newspaper articles and photographs in the folder.

"Ireland was a very different place in those days. You just couldn't have a child out of wedlock." Said Orla.

There were more photos of her mother and her famous fashion creations. There were pictures of her mother in the 60s and pictures of her with Sir Freddie Laker and her sister on a yacht in Majorca. There were pictures of them holidaying in Spain, where Rosie's husband and she had been, all those years ago in Sotogrande, probably all at the same time. How she ached to have known her. She was obviously a very successful and popular woman. If only she had known she might have become a fashion designer or model herself. She had so nearly followed that route but did not have the confidence to take it any further.

"Why didn't she ever marry or have more children?" Rosie asked.

"She wasn't that interested in men after Leonard to be honest. She could take or leave them. She had her gay friends at the Royal ballet in Dublin whom she designed for. One of her closest friends David died last week. I am afraid I will have to go to the funeral when the christening is on in Dublin. He only found out about your existence a week ago. It is such a tragedy he has died."

They ordered their food, but we could not eat anything. There was so much to discuss. So much to catch up on. Humphrey and Pat said her mum was very much the life and soul of the party, that Rosie reminded them so much of her.

"You even smoke like her," said Pat.

Orla asked if Rosie had been happy. She said that she had had a fortunate, but difficult upbringing. She had always wanted to get in touch but didn't want to hurt her adoptive mother. They all chatted in to the early hours. It was like they had always known each other. It was like Rosie had come home.

They left the restaurant and all piled into Humphry and Pat's large Georgian townhouse in the centre of Macroom. The kitchen had a bar area and they all sat round it. More bottles of wine were opened.

"This was where you mother used to spend many evenings with our friends." Said Humphrey.

They laughed and they sang. Rosie had never been in such pleasurable company. Pat got out more photos of her mother, more poignant ones showing her mother with cancer, when she lost the use of her left hand. These were her mother's true friends. The only thing dividing them was her English accent.

"Now I can see where your love of drinking came from." Said her husband.

They went back to the hotel in the early hours of the morning agreeing to all meet up the next day.

"Welcome home Rosie, welcome home."

The next day Rosie woke up and climbed out of bed. She immediately reached for the red folder which was on the coffee table and climbed onto the window seat to smoke a cigarette through the window and read again the contents. It was time to tell the children what was going on. They were going to see Aunty Orla today as a family and it would be impossible for them not to see the family resemblance.

They went downstairs and each ordered a full Irish Breakfast, consisting of black and white pudding which they had never had before.

"We are going to see someone today, who we met last night and who means a lot to your mummy. You see grandma is not mummy's real mummy, as mummy was adopted as a baby by her. Mummy's real mummy is dead but her sister is alive and she is going to meet us at the hotel this morning and then she is going to drive us to her house. Then we will hopefully grab a bite to eat at the local pub. Mummy has a folder upstairs with photos of her real mummy. She was a very beautiful lady."

Rosie didn't know if her younger children really understood what was going on. Over the forthcoming weeks they were to ask many searching questions. They were about to discover their new family and the Irish roots that her children would inherit. Orla was quite sure that her father was Irish which made her one hundred per cent Irish.

Orla greeted them later on at the hotel. She drove them through some beautiful craggy countryside towards the west coast of Ireland.

"I'm near the village of Ballyvourney which is famous for newly weds passing through."

They turned off the main road and followed a windy road up a hill through the woods towards her house, which was a large Georgian house perched on the top of the bank with views stretching for miles over the undulating countryside. The house had a small turning circle to park your cars in the front.

"Welcome to my humble abode."

"It's beautiful." Rosie said "It reminds me of my husband's parents house when they were married."

Orla led them in to the kitchen and made them all a cup of tea.

"There's a picture I'd like you to see on the wall."

Rosie walked towards the picture. It was a beautiful watercolour of Paris in the winter. It was signed by Miriam.

Donald proceeded to show all the children the rabbit warrens in the garden. Orla showed them the work she had done to the house.

"This was the house that Donald grew up in. We moved back here a few years ago. It needed a massive amount of work doing to it. It's on the market now, because Donald wants us to live in Spain. I don't suppose you want to buy it?"

They spent a long time at the house. Rosie was a little worried they were going to miss lunch. In France you need to get to a restaurant by 2 o'clock if you want any chance of being served food. This was Ireland though, where she forgot food is served all day as in England. They eventually made their way down to the pub and grabbed a table outside. They'd banned smoking in the pubs in Ireland so the only place they could smoke was outside. The rest of the gang joined them and more wine and food was ordered. The sun was shinning that day, and whilst they were there many wedding parties came and went.

After a long day they retired back to the bar at the Castle. Some of the guests were starting to arrive for the christening the next day.

"I won't be able to see you tomorrow because I have to go to a funeral." Said Orla. "But I want to see you and the children before you go, so shall I meet you at the airport in Cork at midday before you get your flight?"

"That's fine by us. We'll see you then."

The first drink they ordered was a gin and tonic. They didn't realize that in Ireland it was customary for everyone to buy everyone a round of drinks. Before they knew it her husband and Rosie had eight gin and tonics and pints on the table.

"I can't drink this many gin and tonics. Normally I switch to wine after the first drink." If they thought the first night was a long one the second was even longer. They sat up talking with their new found friends until 5 o'clock in the morning. Everyone started singing their known Irish songs.

The following day fell from one alcoholic blur to another. The service was to be held at the local Catholic Church in Macroom. About a hundred people attended. Outside many people commented on what a fascinating story Rosie's was and how glad they were that they could make it. It seemed touching that the weekend should culminate in a christening, the religious celebration of a birth. Fidelma's mother came over to Rosie and said.

"I am glad that I was of some help. I am so sorry to hear that your mother died. We were just so lucky that we could get hold of Orla."

The service was beautifully done. They weren't quite sure where to sit at first as they weren't really family and didn't want to impose. By the time they got to the reception they were feeling a bit awkward, because clearly Fidelma and Nick were caught up with their friends and the only other people they knew were Humphrey and Pat. They needn't have worried. Everyone was extremely welcoming. The children got on with all the other children. They met people who were in to property development or art or both. They talked about Rosie's extraordinary story and their meeting at the Colombe D'or. They talked about Ireland and the places to go and see when they were next over.

"What's the secret to Irish gravy?" Rosie asked.

"They put too much fat in it."

They stayed up that evening until 5 o' clock in the morning.

"I don't think my liver can take much more of this," said her husband." Perhaps we should check out tomorrow and go somewhere else. We can always come back again in the next few weeks. What do you say?"

"That sounds a great idea. I spoke to someone about my passion for cooking and they mentioned that Kinsale which is half an hour from here is the food capital of Ireland. Perhaps we can find a hotel there to stay in. We're still meeting Orla to say goodbye the following day."

The next day they checked out of the Castle in Macroom and drove down the coast to Kinsale. It was a beautiful sunny day again and as they turned the corner for the port they saw the village sign for Kinsale "Twinned with Juan les Pins France"

"How extraordinary." Rosie exclaimed. "Of all the places to be twinned with. That's the place we went to when your father died."

They checked into a hotel on the seafront and took a look round the village. It had an old feel to it with little brightly coloured houses squashed together round the port with lots of fishing boats. There were little pubs and boats dotted around the place. The seagulls flew and cried in the skies. It was a Sunday so the place was very busy with people walking round with ice creams or fish and chips. Her husband noticed that all the Irish girls they saw had a certain look about them that reminded him of Rosie when she was younger, brownish blondish hair with green eyes. Just behind a small fairground they found a lovely fish restaurant. There was a small queue, but from looking at the menu and the food they could see why there was a queue and decided to wait.

Eventually they got a table outside and they ordered "moules marinieres" for the children and lobsters for themselves. That afternoon they took a short drive over the estuary to a pub on the other side and discovered a beautiful beach round the corner. That day they were to receive a phone call from the agent in London to say that the tenants wanted to buy the London house. They had seen what they thought to be the beginnings of a property crash in Ireland as there had been too many new builds, and thought nothing of it. Little did they know that a world crash was about to happen. They rejected an offer which with hindsight they should have taken. Later that evening they dined in the hotel restaurant and went for a well earned early night.

The following day the children wanted to go swimming in the hotel swimming pool, before making their way back to the airport.

"We don't want to do that. We've got a pool at home in France which you can use anytime you want. A pool is a pool at the end of the day." Rosie said.

"Why don't we do a bit more exploring."

"Let's look at the map over breakfast and then take a drive."

They decided they would take a drive round the headland to a place called Old Head and then the beach. They couldn't go far as they needed to get to the airport. They took the road which followed the cliffs along the sea to Old Head. The scenery was dramatic on the drive there. They drove as far as they could to the peninsula, to the gateway of a golf course. They then got out of the car and walked to the cliffs' edge.

"Be careful children, it is a very steep fall. Don't go too close to the edge."

The grassland gave way to an enormous steep jagged black cliff. The sea below was crashing against the rocks. It was very windy up there. It felt as if they were on the edge of the world, where land meets sea. They took some photos of the children staring out to sea.

"It is beautiful up here." Rosie said.

They then took the car to the beach below. The tide was out so the sea was a long way from them. Her youngest began to look for shells and pebbles to take back for their bathrooms in Saint Paul. They could smell the salty sea air on their lips as the wind blew off the ocean.

"Time to go." Rosie said.

They drove to the airport and dumped the hire car at the hire car place. As they entered the airport Orla was waiting for them at the café before departures. Rosie's children ran up to her and gave her a big hug.

"I've got some little Irish mementos for you, some Irish jackets, Irish flute, an Irish doll and a Bridgid's cross which is meant to protect your house. I didn't know what else to get you in such a short period of time."

"Oh Aunty Orla you needn't have gone to all this trouble."

"No, I wanted them to take something of Ireland with them."

"Will you move to Spain do you think?"

"I don't know. Donald wants to move there and it all depends on whether we sell the house. I do feel my roots are here though."

She then asked where they had been yesterday and that day. Rosie said that they had stayed in Kinsale, the night before, at a lovely hotel on the port. They had discovered a lovely fish restaurant to have lunch at. She then explained that they had visited Old Head. She was about to ask a question when Orla said.

"Your mother's ashes were scattered there."

Rosie's heart skipped a beat. No one had told her this. It was extraordinary that they had been drawn there. She'd heard of ashes being scattered in the sea in France. It seemed so fitting that she was scattered in the sea and that now she too would be able to look at the ocean and know that she was part of it wherever she might be.

Eventually they had to say their goodbyes, which was a tearful event. Rosie often saw families saying goodbye to loved ones at the airport. She had always envied them. Her adoptive mother had never waved goodbye to her at the airport. They said goodbye, but not in the emotional sense. This goodbye was so touching because they didn't want to say goodbye. They had only just found each other.

"Stay in touch and come back soon." She said.

As they boarded the plane Rosie noticed the name of the plane was "St Fidelma"

"It's a funny old world."

Many Saints had conspired to make things happen over those last few weeks. Saint Rosalie's day in the Catholic calendar, her birthday, Saint Paul in France where they had bought their house and now Saint Fidelma, the woman who had brought them all together in the Colombe D'Or in France. If ever Rosie believed in God, she did now. Her prayers had finally been answered before her fortieth birthday. It was the best birthday present she could ever have. Her inner soul was now at peace.

EPILOGUE

T HE HARDEST THING about finding her real mum was always going to be telling her adoptive mother. Since her stroke she had been struggling in her apartment in Little Venice with a carer who came in three hours a day to help her. By now she could not walk unaided without a stick or a walking frame. Her flat was on the fifth floor and the lift often broke down. With hindsight she should have bought a garden flat years before, but she had always been so stubborn. Just as she refused to come and live with them in France, so she refused to accept, the stairs and the lift were a liability to her and to others. In some ways her refusal to come to live with Rosie was a blessing as she did not think they would have been able to cope with three small children and a grandparent in tow. The amount of care she needed now was unsustainable.

To make the flat safe after her stroke they had to disconnect the cooker, as there were a number of people that complained about the smell of gas in her apartment. After a series of falls in attempting to get to the toilet a commode was installed in her bedroom. Bath rails and a special toilet seat were installed in her bathroom. An automatic dialing system was installed on the telephone as the sight having gone in one eye made it difficult for her to use. She could only eat cold foods from now on as she did not have the cooker. Her daily meals consisted of cold quiche or cheese and a series of ensure drinks to make sure she put some weight on. There were a whole series of tablets she was meant to take for her bones and constitution which she was often remiss in taking.

Day in day out she lived an existence in her apartment which could only be described as an existence. She rarely went out as it was too dangerous. They'd bought a wheelchair for her, but she refused to go out in it with the carer. Rosie could not understand why she didn't want to go out and see the sunlight or smell the flowers. She could even have gone to the theatre or the church with a little forethought. Life was for living, not for dying even if your body had given up on you. Her carer was called Bridget and was very caring but her adoptive mother would always complain about her, not doing enough housework for her, or having the television on all the time. Because her adoptive mother was paying for her she wanted to treat her like staff. The joke was that this person was the one person who was giving her her dignity.

Rosie would try and telephone her adoptive mother from France, but it was always a disaster. She wouldn't hold the earpiece to her ear properly or understand what she was saying. It was different when Rosie saw her. She could have quite lucid conversations with her until she got tired and had to go to sleep. Rosie always dreaded staying with her as it felt like staying in what she used to call "the Morgue". Even before her stroke the flat had been pretty depressing. Rosie was to soon learn that her mother's dread of food and nice things stemmed from depression.

When Rosie got home from Ireland her stomach felt sick with anxiety. She knew she had to tell her adoptive mum what happened, but also knew that she wasn't as cognitive as she had been before her stroke. Would this trigger another stroke perhaps?

Only a month before on one of the many occasions Rosie had phoned her, there had been no answer, so she had to call the police who had broken the door down. Social Services were now worried at the level of care she was getting and now wanted to see Rosie. She couldn't put off an impending trip any longer.

"Just take a bottle of wine and order a Chinese take away when you go to see her and tell her that you didn't go looking for your mum, but she found you." Said her husband.

"You do see why I have to tell her don't you?"

"Of course I do."

"I can't not mention Ireland or the people we met. What if the children come out with it when they see her? I haven't telephoned her for two weeks because of what has happened which she will find strange in itself as I usually phone every few days. I just didn't know what to say."

Rosie booked the flights to go to London. She felt so guilty. She felt as if she'd gone behind her back. It was as if she was finally admitting to her that her real mother mattered. But how could she be jealous when her real mother was dead? It seemed so unfair that all these people who wanted to live, like her husband's father and her mother had died and yet her adoptive mother who wanted to die was still living.

Rosie did as her husband suggested go to the local Tescos in Clifton Gardens and bought a bottle of wine.

"Customer number 4 please."

The supermarkets in England had really moved on since they were in France. The choice of food and the service was unbelievable.

She stocked up with a few provisions for her as well and then bought her some flowers from the florist, some beautiful white roses. She proceeded round to her mansion block which was on a very busy road. When she got there, the lift was broken and she had to climb up the five flights of stairs to her apartment. Whilst she was fit even these stairs wore her out.

She rang the doorbell and waited for her adoptive mum to come to the door. She was slow getting to the door using her Zimmer frame.

"Hi mum, how are you?"

"Lovely to see you Love."

Rosie grabbed her tiny frame and gave her a hug. She was so skinny these days you could feel every bone sticking out of her body.

"I've brought you some flowers"

"Oh they are lovely"

"Now sit down whilst I find a vase and open this bottle of wine." She said waving her hands "No I'll do this, you just concentrate on sitting yourself down without falling over."

Rosie went in to the tiny galley kitchen and placed the roses in a vase with some water. She opened the fridge. Nearly everything in there was past its' sell by date. She took a mental note to remind the carer. Next to the fridge were stacks and stacks of unopened tablets supplied by NHS direct. She fetched two glasses and walked across the creaky hallway to the living room where her adoptive mother was struggling to sit down. She was using all her strength, just to make this simple manoeuver. The carpet was frayed and tatty stuck together with bits of masking tape. The spider plant which Rosie's original mother gave to her adoptive mother was dead long ago from no watering. She sat down next to her in one of the leather armchairs. They chatted for awhile and sipped their glasses of wine. Her adoptive mother always swigged hers just a little too quickly, and Rosie had to be careful not to give her too much to drink or she might fall over.

"I'll order a take away shall I?"

"Oh yes please."

She ordered the take away and when it arrived they sat at the table, next to the french doors opening out on to the balcony overlooking Maida Vale. They could hear the roar of the traffic below and the occasional police sirens from Harrow Road Police Station. The mansion block opposite was all lit up and you could just make out the illuminated Post Office Tower in the distance.

"Mummy I've got something important to tell you. I'm telling you because I know you sometimes doubt your faith and whether there is really a God out there, but I now know for sure there is. I have never gone in search of my real mother for fear of hurting you. I know you've always said that you wouldn't mind if I went looking for her, but once I got married and had children of my own I gave up looking for her. You must not be hurt by what I am going to tell you because I love you very much and will always love you."

Rosie paused to check that her adoptive mother was understanding her.

"You know you told me that my mother would always be easy to find with a surname like Sullivan-Cody, well I was in a restaurant in Saint Paul and we met some Irish people and I asked them if they knew of her and they did. They rang me the following week to tell me that unfortunately she died of breast cancer in 1988, aged 45, but that I could still meet some of her friends. So we flew over to Cork last week and met them, and my mother's sister Orla. I'm telling you all this because the coincidences, every one of them are extraordinary, and if you don't believe in God then surely you do now"

Her mother paused for awhile. Rosie thought she understood what she had said. She could not gauge whether what she had told her had affected her or not. Eventually after chewing her lip for quite some time she said.

"I'm sorry she is dead darling."

Rosie hugged her and they carried on talking for a time and then she got tired and she helped put her to bed. She told her again that she still loved her and that nothing had changed, just that she had a wonderful experience in Ireland. She knew in her heart of hearts that if she wanted to look for anyone it would be her real father as she had not grown up with one. That night she telephoned her husband and told him her reaction. He agreed that as her real mother was now dead, she posed no threat to her adoptive mother.

Rosie stayed at the flat that night in her old bedroom. It was looking tired now. There was hardly anything of her left in it, just a few old photos, letters and books from her youth. The wheelchair had been stowed behind the curtain, never to be used again. She'd noticed that night that her adoptive mother was getting frailer. Her mind was still there, but her body wasn't keeping up with her. Rosie pondered that night how she'd spent all those nights in that apartment, growing up in an old existence. How had she managed to grow up "normal". Despite all her adoptive mother's mannerisms, she'd still retained her real parents' genes.

The following morning Social Services paid a visit. Her adoptive mother could no longer afford a private carer and now needed support three times a day, to help her get up in the morning, give her, her lunch and put her to bed. They confirmed that Westminster City Council would pay the majority of these fees with a small contribution from her adoptive mother. It would mean her mother being looked after by various carers, but still in the confines of her flat. Her adoptive mother was always asked if she would consider some form of secure housing, but she always flatly refused. There was nothing anyone could do because her adoptive mother was still capable of making her own decisions.

Over the following months, her adoptive mother continued to have a series of falls, from getting out of her chair or going to the bathroom at night. Eventually after quite a serious fall where she had been immobile for several hours they admitted her again to St Mary's Hospital Paddington. She was then moved to a rehabilitation unit just off the Harrow Road. This was to be the start of the process of placing her into a nursing home.

"I should have made this decision earlier shouldn't I?" Her adoptive mother said. "I could have saved you all a lot of bother."

Rosie couldn't say that she should have because she knew she wanted to stay in her own place for as long as she could. Who wouldn't? It was just that they could have made the decision together as to which nursing home would have suited her. They could have looked at the facilities of nursing homes in the country, which were inevitably better than ones in Inner London. Rosie had recently looked at a nursing home in Cheltenham which was better than the one she was now in with glorious views over the Cotswold landscape, but she was too frail now too infirm, and in any event her adoptive mum was not one for beautiful views, beautiful gardens or beautiful houses. Rosie now realized her adoptive mother lost the love for everything beautiful when her husband died.

But one thing Rosie has learnt from this journey is the unconditional love her adoptive mother had for her. It was maybe selfish, but without Rosie she would have had no life. All Rosie's life she had been embarrassed by her adoptive mother yet she gave her the best start in life. She had been very fortunate, because of her love. She gave her all the tools she needed to enter the real world and help deal with it and people.

This became none so more apparent to her when they were considering what to do with her adoptive mother's flat when she went in to the nursing home. Her adoptive mother had been in the nursing home for about a year and the flat had always been in trust for Rosie and her half brothers. Her adoptive mother had already sold a large portfolio of shares to help out Rosie and her half brothers. They kept the flat for her, whilst she was in the nursing home, just in case she couldn't bear the nursing home and wanted to move back to the flat. If Rosie were being honest, having experienced the nursing home, no one wants to go there.

It was like a funny farm with varying degrees of senility. She didn't know how the staff did it. When she went to see her adoptive mother there, she knew she had no choice but to be there. She needed twenty four hour care which only a nursing home could provide. Rosie's heart went out to her for agreeing to be in the nursing home in the first place. But it was the only place she know where she was safe and where she would not harm herself.

"Mummy, you know your flat, well at some time in the future we are going to have to sell it, do you understand?"

The lawyers had told Rosie that she would have to get her assessed as to her capability to make this decision as even though they had a power of attorney, if she wanted to return to the flat even if it wasn't in her best interests, she could. A specialist in Parkinson's disease went to see her as did many other specialists. These visits were heartbreaking because Rosie would have to fly in and see her mother and know that the precious time she wanted to spend with her was being taken up with these other people. One of the specialists on such a visit, saw her mother's eyes look at her and said

"She really loves you, you know."

That comment really touched Rosie. She won't call her mother, her adoptive mother any more. She is her mother. She needs her love now more than ever. She's scared of dying, She doesn't have to say as much. Her body is letting her down but her soul is willing her to live.

She agreed to sell the flat and Rosie returned to France. Then she received an email from the lawyer saying she was quite adamant that she did not want to sell the flat in the current market. Rosie's mind went in to head spin. Why was she doing this to her? Was she back to the cantankerous mum she knew the one that deliberately wanted to be awkward. The one she had mixed feelings for?

"Your mum probably was just confused because you weren't with her. Don't take this personally Rosie. I'm sure she didn't mean it." Her husband said.

And she was confused, because when Rosie went to see her again she said.

"Oh I'm sorry, I've been saying the wrong things again darling."

Rosie agreed to be with her next time. You see her mother never trusted anyone except Rosie. She literally was the only person she relied upon. She would never see any good in anyone, because Rosie was to learn, life had not been kind to her. Everywhere she had turned in life she had been met by a brick wall.

The flat was sold and they had only two weeks to empty the flat and retain what they could of her belongings. They took the family to London and camped out at the apartment. They had agreed that the items of furniture should be sold at Christies. There was no way they could get these down to France and anyway they didn't have any room for them at their French house. Rosie had always had the key to her mother's trunk where she kept all her personal effects, but she had never had the courage to open it. Her entire life was in that trunk.

Rosie gingerly opened the trunk and noticed it was full of documents and boxes. Three large files of correspondence with lawyers. Boxes with medals from the First and Second World War. Trinkets and rings. There was a letter of commendation from King George V. Copies of all her certificates. Newspaper front pages going from 1914, through to the funeral of George V, all the way through to 911. Stamp collections with penny reds and penny blues, coin collections, photographs from the previous century. The most poignant documents she found however were the documents about her adoption and her father's death.

Reading through those documents, Rosie realized the trauma her mother had faced. Her utter despair at trying to have a child and subsequent attempts to adopt a child. She saw a different side to the story. In some ways her mother had been utterly selfish in her quest for her, but who wouldn't when you knew her suffering? There were documents that she read that were quite disturbing in the aftermath of her father's death. Yet this was someone who had lost her husband at the tender age of 45. She had kept these documents so that Rosie might one day see her side of the story. When her father died she wrote.

"*It seems that there are various levels of personality, probably some people have more levels or layers than others. And some people move from one level to another more easily than others. Anyway each person carries on the greater part of his life at one particular level, and the levels at which different people operate vary. I suppose there are deep unconscious pulls and balances which decide the level of operation.*

At last we found one another. There were superficial difficulties and problems, but we had a deep affinity, we found real love and peace together. Then we were torn apart, why? Because I used to think that death was a purely physical accident, a matter of chance, that there was no plan about it. I don't now, why do some die, and others recover? How was it that one heard of a number of cases during the war of men knowing that their number was up? Is it right to try and think about these things, or is it useless, and better to plod along and take what comes without much thought.

I want him to remain a real part of my life, as he still is at present. I can't bear the thought of losing my remembrance and awareness of him. It has taken me a long time to accept his death, and though I dared not speak of it to anyone, I kept expecting him to come back, against all reason. Some days I just ache and long for him, so much it drives out all other things. But sometimes I seem to be talking to him, telling him about things that have happened in quite an ordinary way, but if I notice and start thinking about it and doubting it, it goes. I find, in remembering, that holidays come back the clearest, the happy times at Velden, and that lovely day in Salzburg, for instance, come back more clearly than everyday life. I don't know why. And I wonder what I was like, and why he loved me, because I've very little recollection of myself and the times I do remember, I was mostly being horrid. I want to live here for the rest of my life, I don't know if I'll be able to, but I hope so. And I hope it will always be a place he can come back to if he wants to, and feel at home and loved still.

Is it true that we hate those who are like ourselves? It's a daunting thought. Think of the person you detest the most, and see if you can face the thought that you are like him or her. No? Lets play something else!

What do people mean when they say they have a vocation, or call to do something. I've often wondered. They just have a burning desire to do it, so why not say so? Why has anything like that to be made to sound noble, or moral? I think that's where a lot of the trouble lies, people wanting to deck themselves out with righteous intentions for doing what they want to do anyway. We very rarely know our own true motives, but it's fashionable, in certain quarters, to say you want to help people and so forth. What would you do if no one needed helping? Isn't it best to do what's nearest, even if its not very onerous or self denying, and take delight in life whenever we can. Soper and people like him, talk as if the Kingdom of God just consists of helping others. That's a part of it, I daresay, but I'm sure it's something far grander and gayer than that."

In some ways these writings were profoundly disturbing. However in the context of when they were written, you could understand her tortured soul. Her mother was struggling on her own in this world. She was desperate to find comfort in God when God had let her down. Some time later she was to convert to Catholicism. She was deeply worried at the time that such a conversion would prevent her reuniting with her father in heaven.

Rosie found some old photos of her family which she took with her when she went to see her. She hoped that she would find solace in those photos. Some were of her mother as a little girl playing cricket with her brother. Some were of the bank where she grew up in Boroughbridge in Yorkshire. Others were of her father and her Grandfather. Her father had been gassed in the First World War and subsequently went blind. He looked very like her mother. Rosie thought Marjorie had a happy childhood, although she always said she wished she had had a brother or a sister to play with.

Clearing out her mother's flat was one of the hardest things to do as she had hidden everything so that the carers wouldn't steal anything. She was always mistrusting of people. There was family silver, hidden in the fridge, behind wardrobes and hidden in drawers. There were files and files of correspondence of letters from her lawyers. There were the original letters from Rosie's real mother at the time of the adoption. Feeling and touching those letters was one of the hardest things Rosie had to do. This was the only connection she had left with her.

But if truth be told, Rosie will always feel her in St Paul, the place she found her. The next hurdle is finding her father. God knows if he is still alive, but she will do everything in her power to find him, to close this chapter in her life. That story will be another book in the making.